Design Illustration

Design Illustration

Sketching and Shading Techniques

David Beasley
*Head of Graphic Design,
Farnborough College of Technology*

Heinemann Educational Books

Heinemann Educational Books Ltd
22 Bedford Square, London WC1B 3HH

LONDON EDINBURGH MELBOURNE AUCKLAND
SINGAPORE KUALA LUMPUR NEW DELHI
IBADAN NAIROBI JOHANNESBURG
PORTSMOUTH (NH) KINGSTON

ISBN 0 435 75063 1

First published 1979
Reprinted 1981, 1982, 1984, 1985, 1986 (twice), 1987

British Library Cataloguing in Publication Data
Beasley, David
Design illustration.
1. Artists' preparatory studies
I. Title
741.2 N7433.5

ISBN 0 435 75063 1

Printed and bound in Great Britain by
Anchor Brendon Ltd, Tiptree, Essex

Preface

This book deals with simple ways of producing pictorial drawings and shading them effectively. The techniques used have been derived from the author's industrial experience and their usefulness to pupil and student alike has been proven during his own teaching career.

The book is presented as a basic course in graphic skills and recognizes the needs of the less artistic student who requires aids and basic rules to improve the quality of his or her drawing. It should be particularly useful to students taking C.S.E., G.C.E., and any other design-based course in schools and colleges.

It is not necessary for the student to have a working knowledge of technical drawing to be able to cope with the contents and exercises of this book. Where an object has been drawn using orthographic projection, each view is labelled to help make interpretation easy. Drawing equipment will be required for some of the exercises; the items listed below are all that are necessary.

Pencils (hard, soft, and a few coloured)
Ruler (to measure millimetres)
Drawing board (with clips, tape, or pins to hold the paper)
T square
45° set square
30°/60° set square

Acknowledgements

I would like to thank my colleagues at Shoreditch College, Brian Mayock, Harry Crane and Bert Storey, who have encouraged me to write this book and have tested the suitability of some of the material.
Acknowledgement is due to the following for illustrations:

Page 4, guinea-pig house; page 21, barrels; and page 30, play boxes—Brenda Jenkins and children of Cippenham Nursery School.
Pages 4 and 11, telephone tables—Chippy Heath Furniture Ltd., High Wycombe.
Page 6, screen walling—Marley Buildings Ltd, Guildford.
Page 6, telephone kiosk by courtesy of the Post Office.
Page 6, washing machine—Servis Domestic Appliances Ltd, Wednesbury.
Page 7, Whiteleaf 4000 kitchen range—Goodearl-Risboro' Ltd, Princes Risborough.
Page 8, house—Mrs A. Foreman.
Page 9, arms—Jill Barker.
Page 10, building bricks—Marion Bellamy.
Page 17 and page 18, bicycles—Mr R. Betts.
Page 20, baby—Mrs B. Andrews.
Page 23, ellipse templates—Technostyl Ltd, Milan.
Pages 28 and 30, building—Mr R. F. Thompson.
Page 29, Maxi car—Austin Morris and Benton and Bowles Ltd.
Page 50, Rota Mini de Luxe mower—Birmid Qualcast (Home and Garden Equipment) Ltd, Derby.
Page 51, building bricks—Shaelyn Ward.
Page 54, posting box by courtesy of the Post Office.
Page 55, hazard cones—Peter Beresford and Bill Pullin.
Page 59, College cup—George Maddison.
Page 68, Porsche 924 car—Porsche Cars Great Britain Ltd, Graham Poulter and Associates and artist, Gavin Macleod.
Page 74, lorry—Stephen King.
Page 74, spanner—Graham Thomas.
Page 75, napkin ring—Terry Wawn.

Contents

1 The perspective view

How can this man obtain a realistic view of the house?

He can do this by placing a glass screen, in this case a window, between himself and the house. By keeping his eye in one position he can draw the view of the house that he requires on the glass using a wax pencil.

Here is the view that he has drawn on the window. The glass is called the **picture plane** since it is the plane on which the picture is drawn.

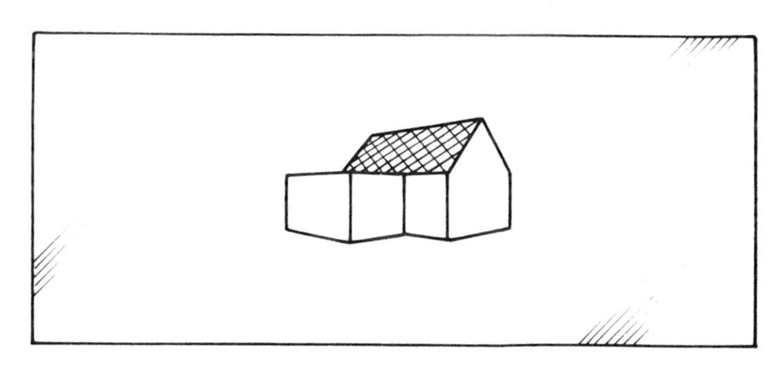

As you can see, if the lines that represent horizontal edges on this drawing are extended, they will meet at two points called **vanishing points** (VP).
A line passing through the two vanishing points will be found to be horizontal

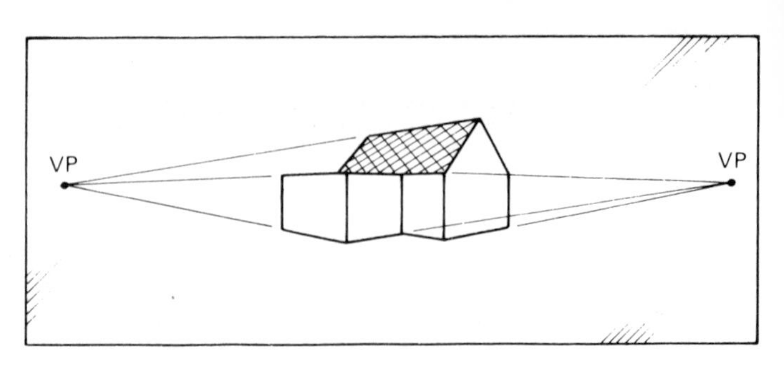

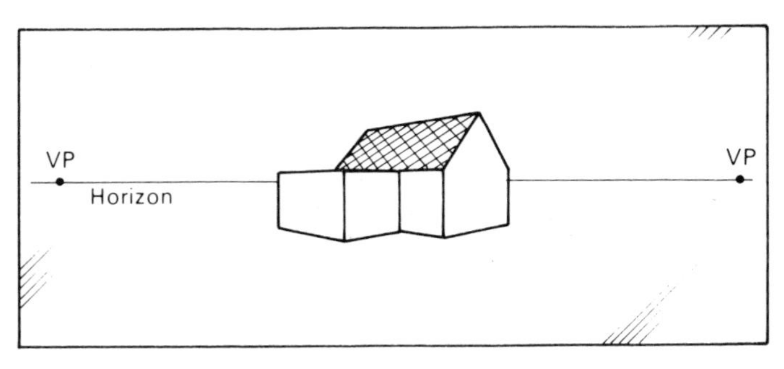

and is called the **horizon**. This is the true horizon. Usually we see a false horizon made up of trees, buildings, and hills, etc. If one or more vanishing points can be found in a picture, it is called a **perspective view**.

Exercise 1a

1 Trace figures (a), (b), and (c) and find the vanishing points and horizon for each.

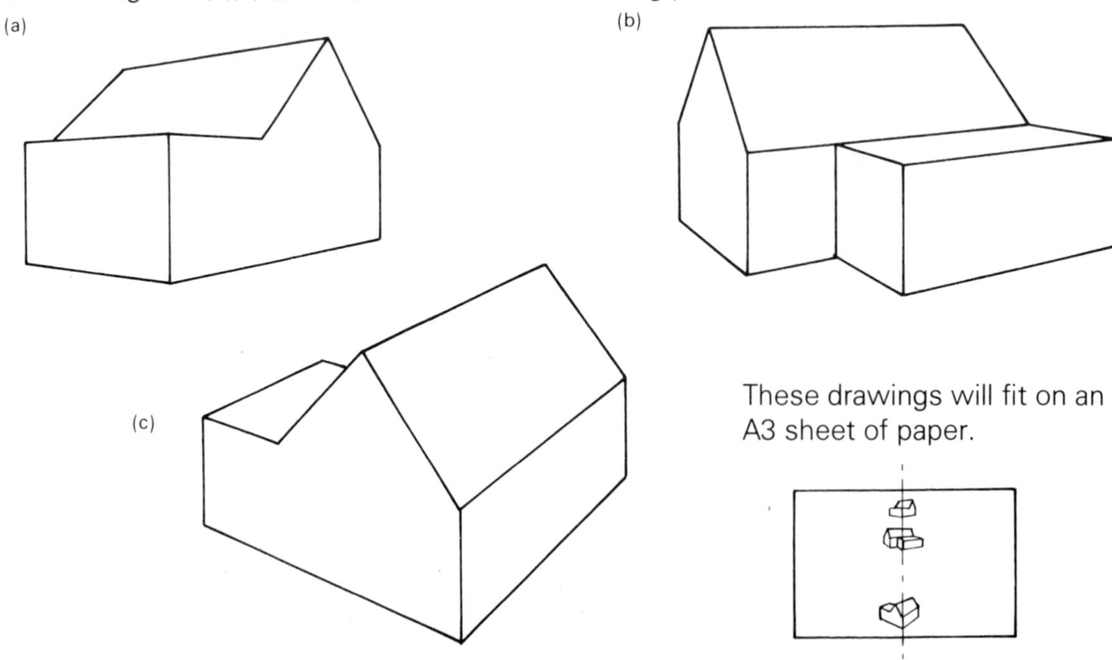

These drawings will fit on an A3 sheet of paper.

2 Obtain three pictures of simple objects from magazines and find the vanishing points and horizon for each. Either attach the pictures to a backing sheet of paper or trace them.

Sketching in perspective

We need to use perspective to make a drawing look realistic and natural. If we had to insert the vanishing points and horizon each time we made a sketch, drawing would become tedious. Also, the view of the object would be very small since the vanishing points would have to fall on the paper like this:

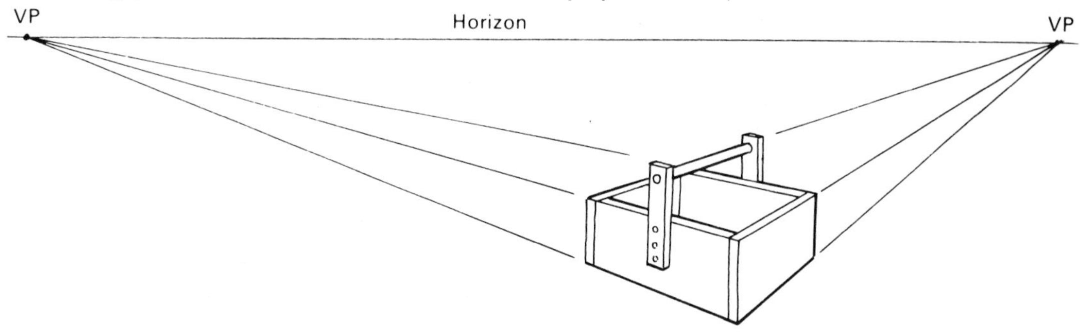

Therefore we must try to imagine where the vanishing points are likely to be and aim our lines towards them. In this way the vanishing points need not be on the paper and the drawing can be bigger, as shown on the right.

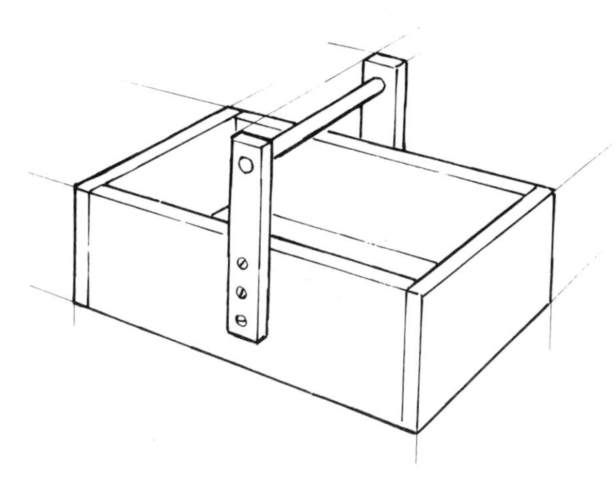

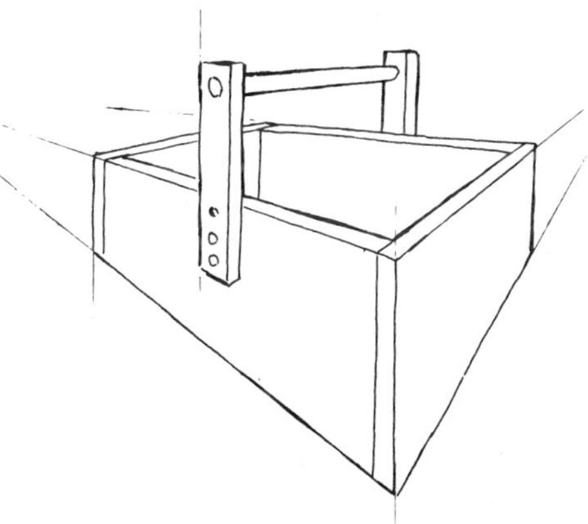

Try not to taper the lines too much, however, as the view tends to become rather distorted.

Exercise 1b

1 Using imaginary vanishing points make freehand perspective sketches of these objects about twice this printed size.

(a) Guinea-pig house.

(b) Book end.

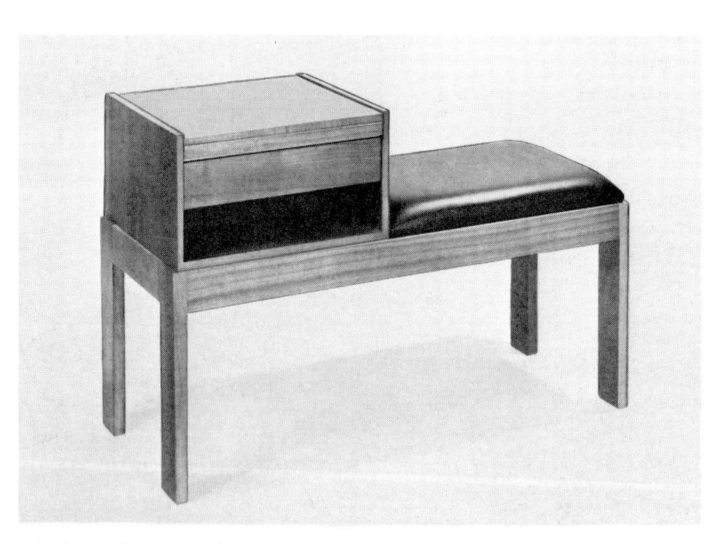

(c) Telephone table.

2 Make perspective sketches using imaginary vanishing points of:

(a) the desk or table on which you are working;
(b) the chair or stool on which you are sitting;
(c) any other suitable piece of furniture which is in the room.

Approximate perspective

A straight edge can be used to help guide your lines towards the imaginary vanishing points. This sequence shows the stages in producing a drawing of a box.

Stage 1

Draw the near corner of the box at an angle which suits your requirements.

Stage 2

Slide the straight edge down so that you can draw the lower edge of the box. In this case the left-hand end has been moved down farther than the right-hand end. This changes the angle and gives the impression that the lines are going to a vanishing point.

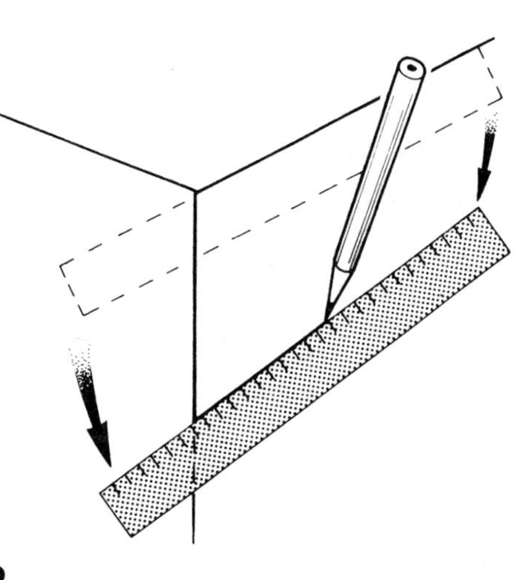

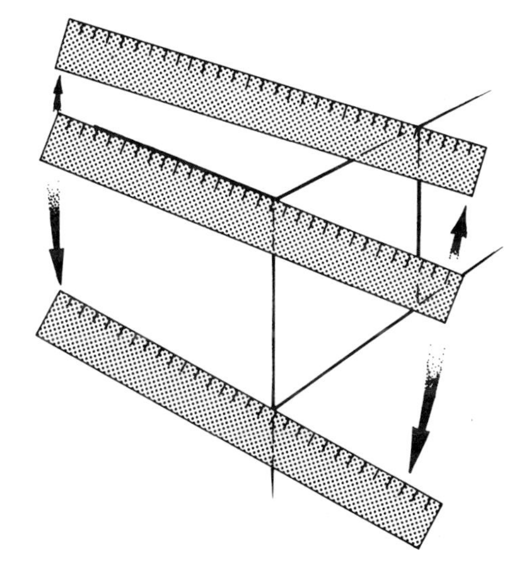

Stage 3

This drawing shows the three positions of the straight edge for the lines in the other direction.

Stage 4

The finished box.

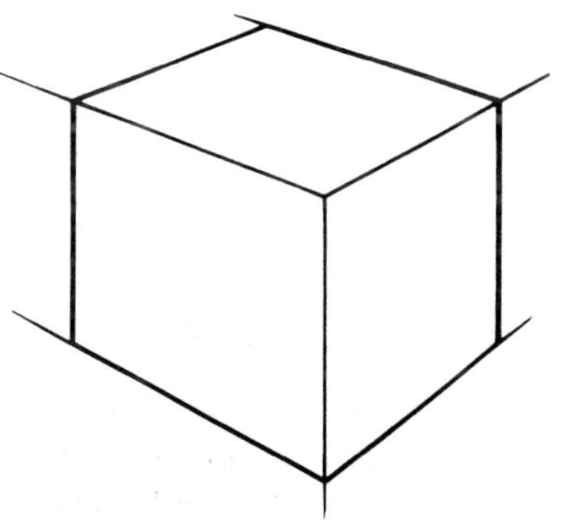

Exercise 1c

Make a perspective drawing of one of these decorative blocks, choosing a viewpoint which clearly shows the three dimensions, height, length, and width, of the block. Use the straight edge method shown on the previous page, remembering to change the angle of the straight edge as you slide it up and down the paper.

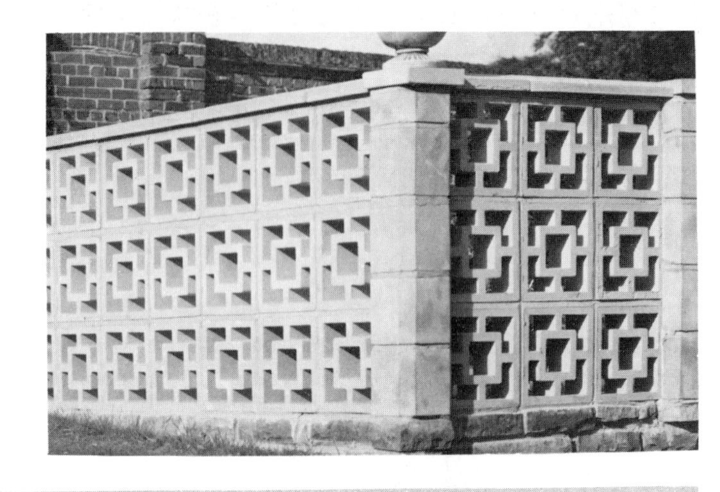

Types of perspective view

Each of our drawings so far has contained two vanishing points. This is not always the case since there can also be one or many vanishing points in a single picture. We will look at the three main types: **one-point**, **two-point**, and **three-point** perspective views, the names being derived from the number of vanishing points involved.

Two-point perspective

These are true two-point perspective views in which only two vanishing points can be traced. The line joining the two vanishing points will pass through the object in this type of perspective view. Turn the page on its side to see that the arrangement of the washing machine is similar to that of the telephone kiosk.

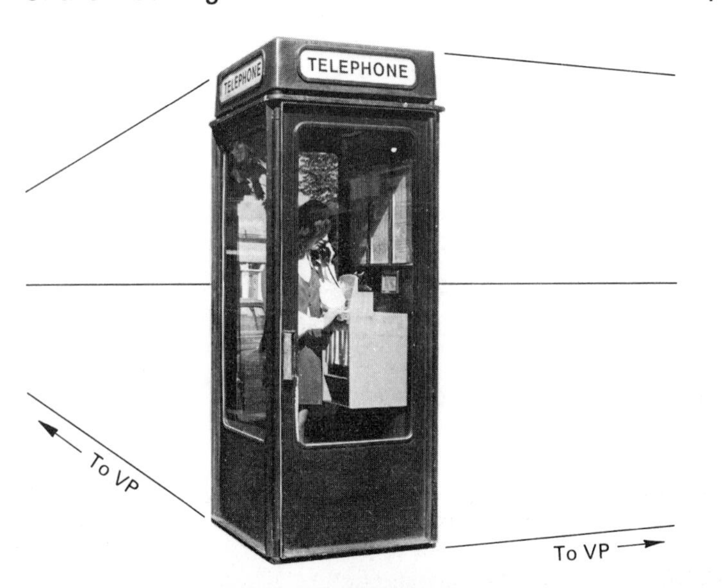

Three-point perspective

When we look up at or down on an object a third vanishing point can be found. As you can see in these pictures, the uprights, i.e. the corners of the building and the legs of the table, are no longer vertical.

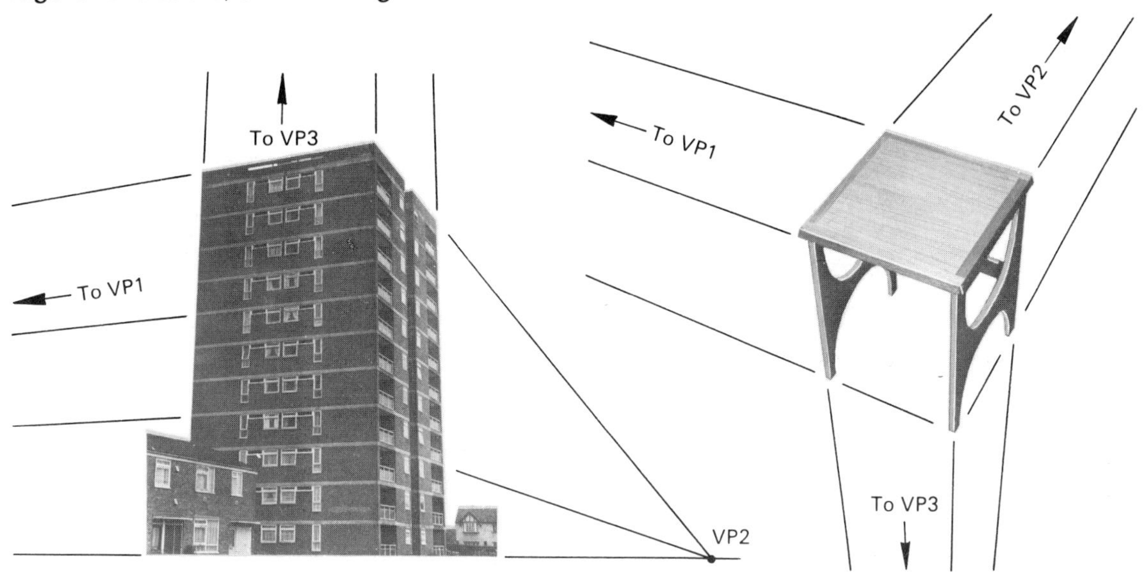

When we are sketching, we normally ignore this third vanishing point since the amount of tapering is usually very slight. This enables us to draw any uprights as vertical lines, which makes the process easier.

One-point perspective

These examples are one-point perspective views in which the single vanishing point lies within the picture. If you can imagine that you are looking through a glass screen in these situations, only the lines that are at right angles to the screen will go to the vanishing point.

Exercise 1d

1 Name the type of perspective view shown in these photographs.

(a)

(b)

(c)

(d)

2 How many vanishing points can you locate in each of these photographs?

(a)

(b)

3 Draw a one-point perspective view of this earthenware tube so that the hole can be seen to go right through.

4 Draw a two-point perspective view of the desk or table on which you are working. Remember that the horizon passes through the object and the two vanishing points lie on the horizon.

2 Drawing in proportion

We can only see the true length of a line if it is at right angles to our line of vision. When we survey an object, the edges that are not at right angles to our line of vision, and therefore do not appear as a true length, but look shorter than they really are, giving the effect of perspective.

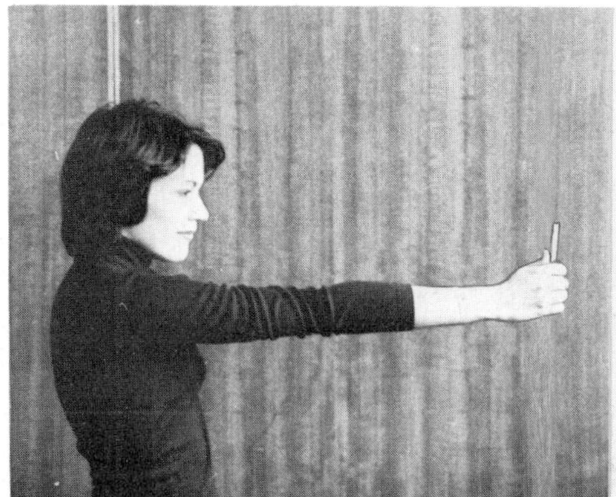

In the first photograph, we can see the whole length of the girl's arm. After she turns towards us, in the second picture, her arm is at an angle to our line of vision and appears shorter, although we know that it is still held out to its full length. The third position shows further apparent shortening of the arm as the angle at which we view increases.
This effect is called **foreshortening**. For example, as we vary our view of this cube, the top edge of the shaded face becomes increasingly foreshortened in the same way as the girl's arm.

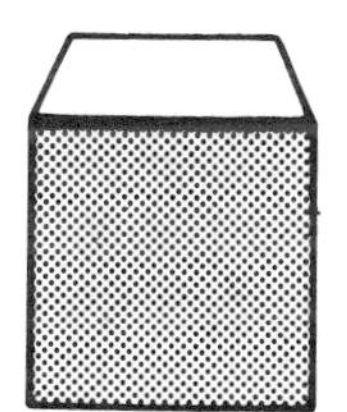
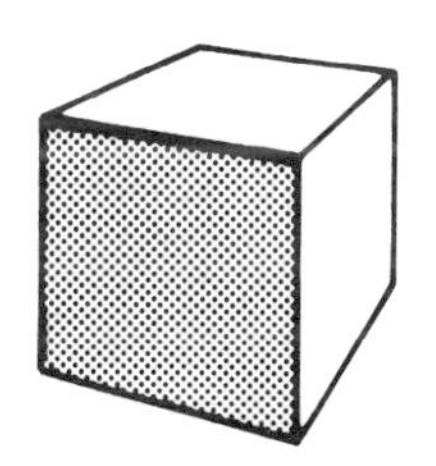
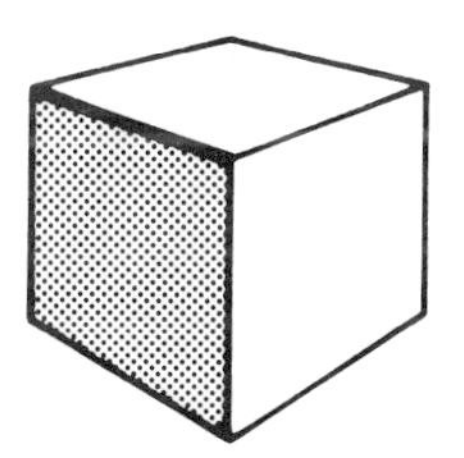
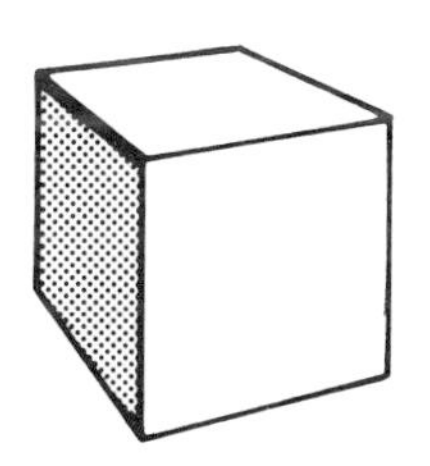

No definite rule can be made as to how much an edge should be foreshortened; the viewer's eye-level in relation to the object and the position of the object are the factors that determine this. Both are usually guessed at where sketching is concerned, and so the amount of foreshortening also has to be approximated.

When sketching, the only rule to bear in mind is that the *more* the edge is turned away the *greater* is the amount of foreshortening.
Therefore in this drawing of a cube, the longest edge is A. B is shorter than A, and C is shorter than B since C is turned away from us to a greater extent than B.

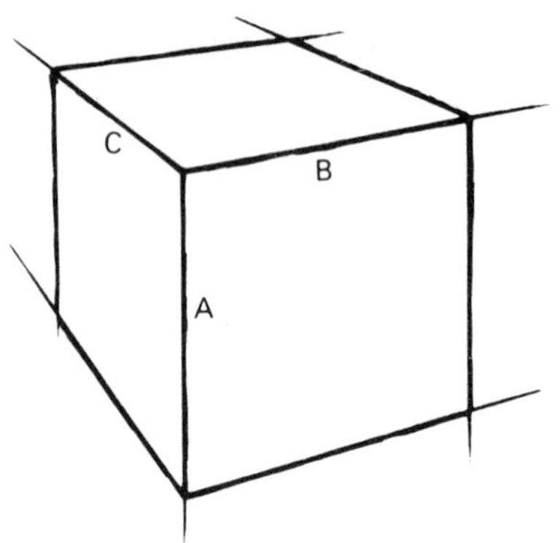

Exercise 2a

1 Sketch four of the building bricks shown in this photograph. Draw the bricks separately but keep each in the same angular position as shown in the picture.

Draw each brick about 60 mm high and bear in mind the previous points about foreshortening.

2 This picture shows a series of windows in a building. As we look from left to right the windows appear to get progressively smaller in height and length: we know this is due to perspective.

Using *both* these pictures for guidance draw three perspective views of a row of six of the child's bricks in line with their faces touching.

Crating objects

To make an effective drawing of an object one must ensure that the proportions of the height, length, and width are reasonably accurate. A good way of doing this is to imagine that the object has yet to be unpacked and that it rests in a box or crate which fits tightly around it. This box is drawn first and modified, if necessary, until the angle of viewing and the proportions are acceptable. Then the more important details can be added, gradually working down to details of a minor nature.

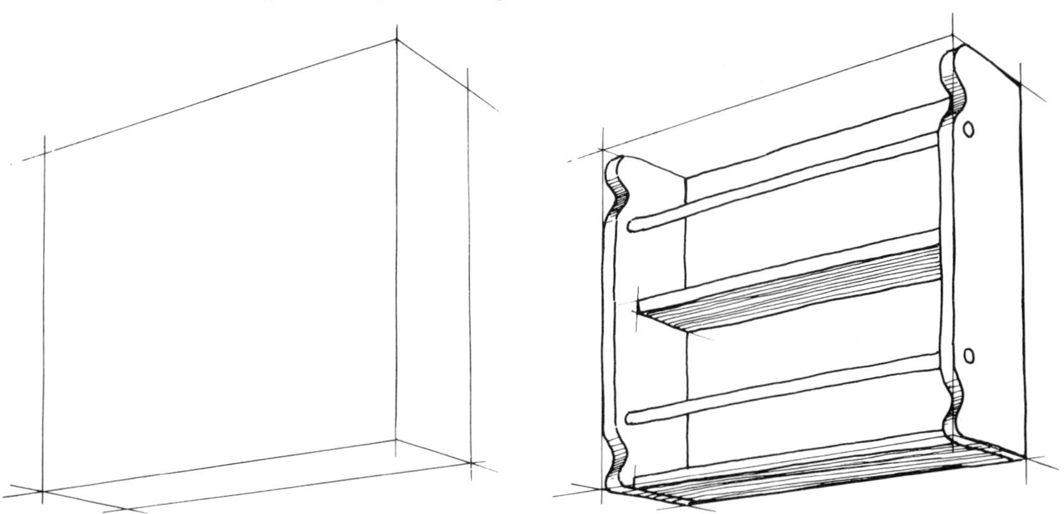

The drawings above show the crate before and after the details of the spice-bottle rack have been added.

Exercise 2b

Draw the crate that would contain this telephone table. Make your drawing about twice this size and, if you wish, keep the same angle as shown in the picture. When you are satisfied with the perspective view of the crate and its proportions, draw the telephone table inside.

Drawing using cubes

To simplify the problem of producing a crate with the correct proportions, we can think of the object we intend to draw in terms of a number of cubes. Few objects can be simplified to the form of one cube but many can be considered as a series of cubes.
The cube is one of the easiest forms to draw, although we should bear in mind the apparent change in the length of the sides due to foreshortening.

Exercise 2c

In a similar way to the examples shown above, construct a perspective view of a suitcase if its proportions are equivalent to one unit high, one and a half units long, and half a unit deep. Refer to this picture for any details you require.

Drawing a toolbox using cubes

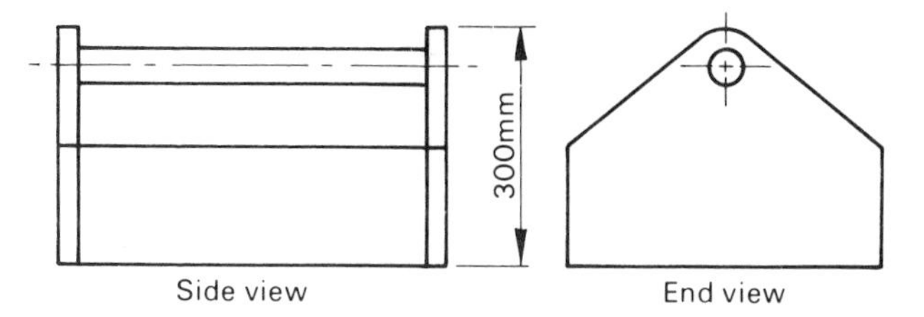

Side view   End view

The measurements of this toolbox are 300 mm high, 400 mm wide, and 500 mm long. These can be simplified into basic proportions of 3 units high, 4 units wide, and 5 units long.

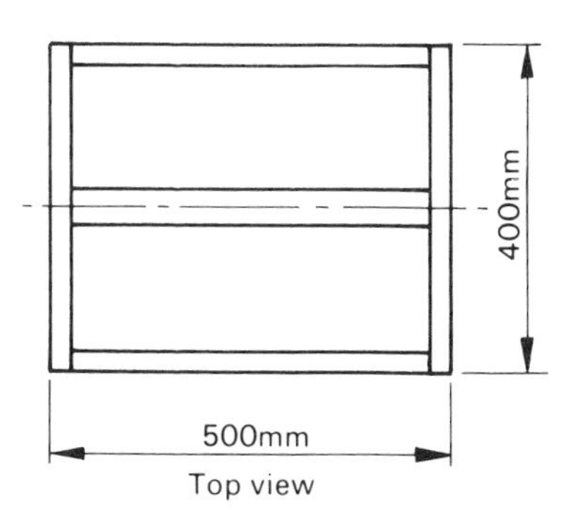

Top view

Stage 1

Draw a cube in a position to suit the required view of the toolbox. We can say that each side of this cube represents 300 mm, the shortest measurement of the toolbox.

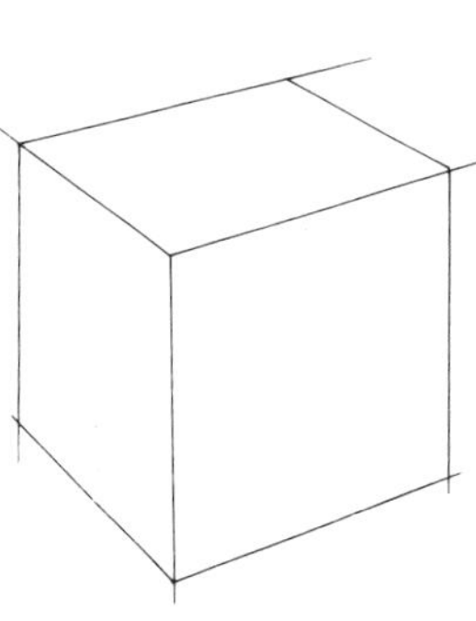

Stage 2

The length of the toolbox, 500 mm, is 200 mm longer than this shortest measurement. Find approximately two thirds of the side of the cube and add it as shown to give the total length.

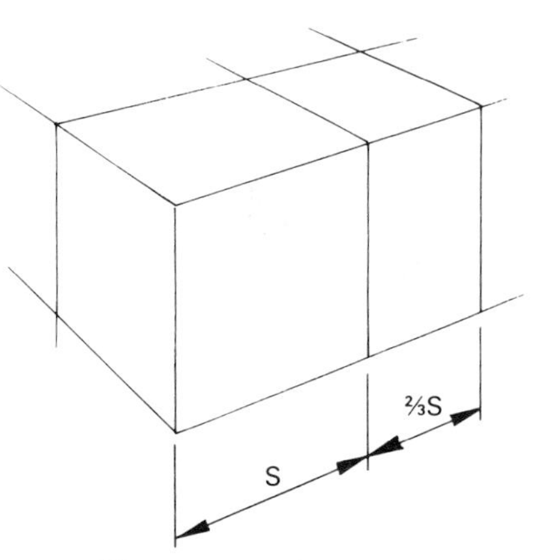

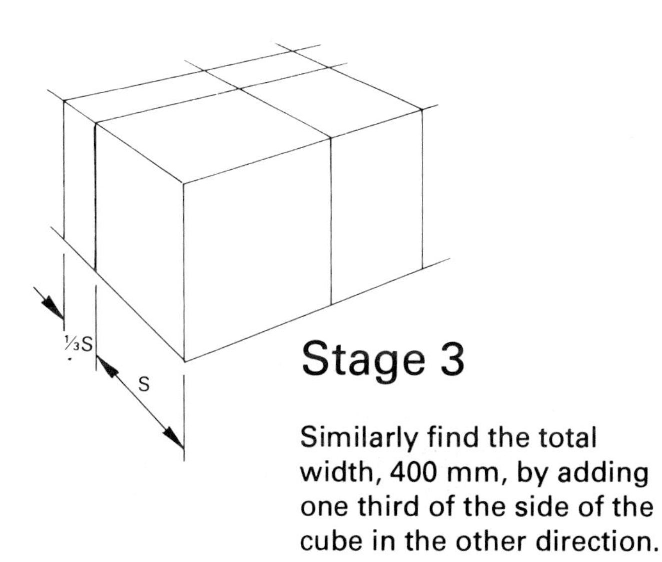

Stage 3

Similarly find the total width, 400 mm, by adding one third of the side of the cube in the other direction.

Stage 4

Within this framework, add the details of the toolbox.

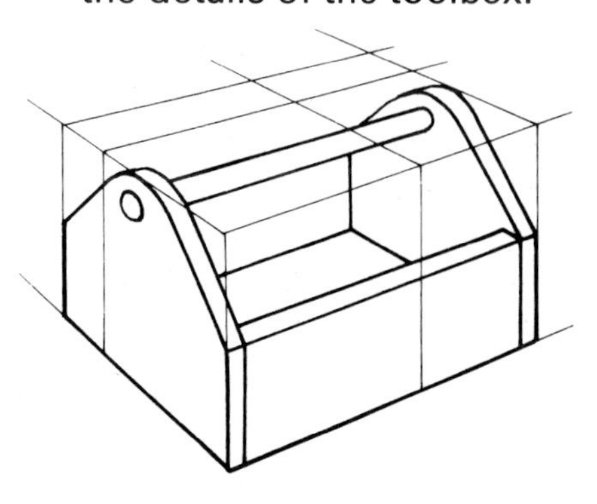

Further proportions using cubes

The following drawings show other ways of finding proportions from the basic cube. The cube must be drawn first, bearing in mind the foreshortened length and width.

In figure 1, the centre of the square face is found by drawing the diagonals. A vertical line drawn through this point will give the proportions for a box of $1 \times 1 \times \frac{1}{2}$.

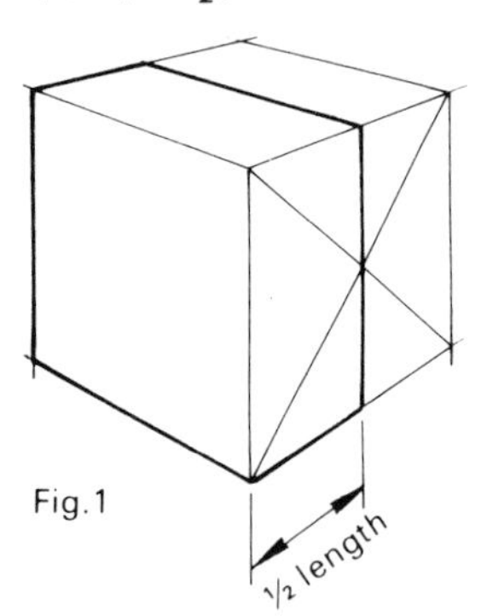

Fig.1

Figure 2 shows a square face divided into two rectangles. The dotted diagonal of one rectangle is continued to meet the top edge that has been extended. This gives the correct amount of foreshortening for the second cube.

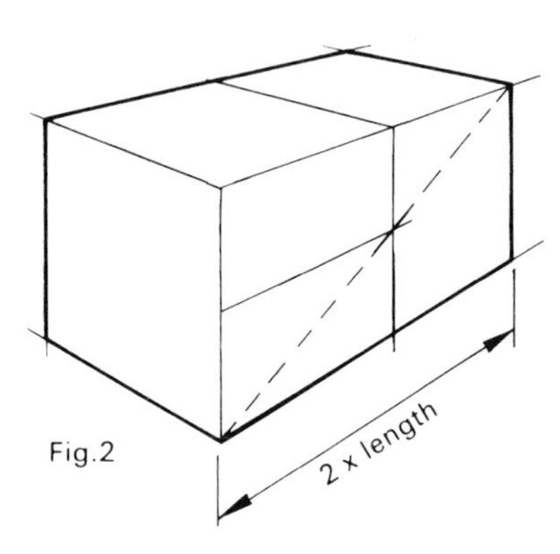

Fig.2

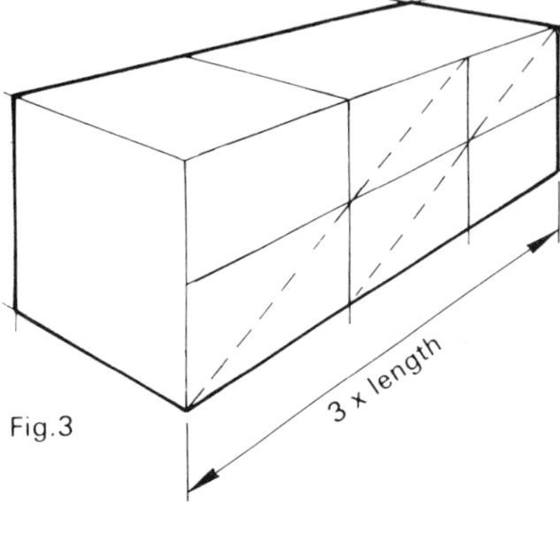

Fig.3

This method is carried one stage further in figure 3 to give three cubes in a row.

Figure 4 is a continuation of figure 1. The half square is divided again to give proportions for a box of $1 \times 1 \times \frac{3}{4}$.

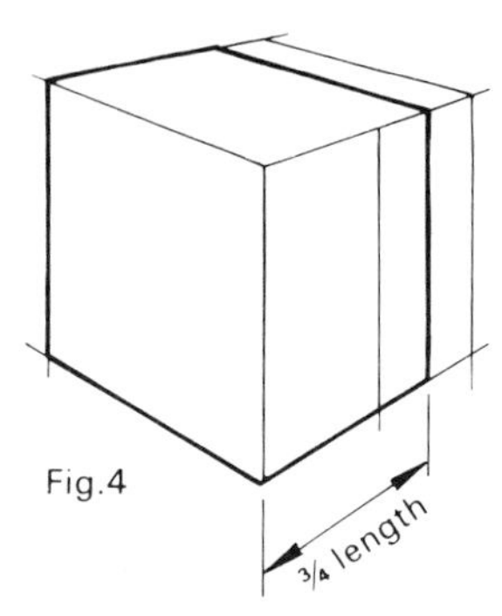

Fig.4

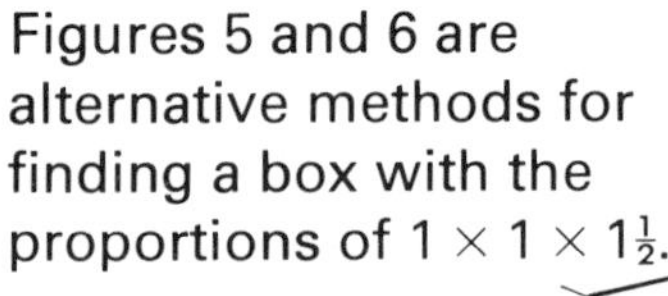

Figures 5 and 6 are alternative methods for finding a box with the proportions of $1 \times 1 \times 1\frac{1}{2}$.

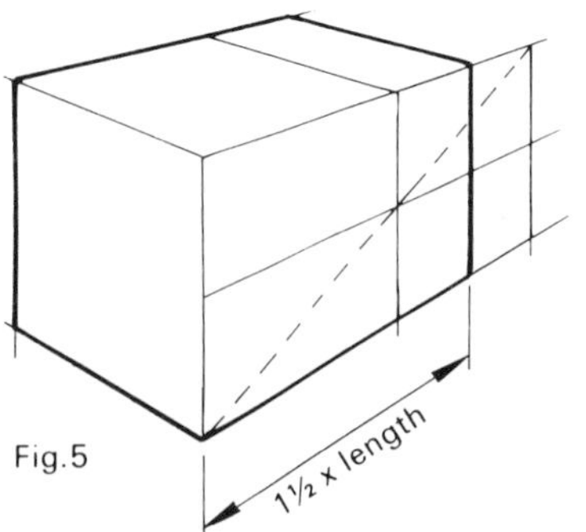

Fig.5

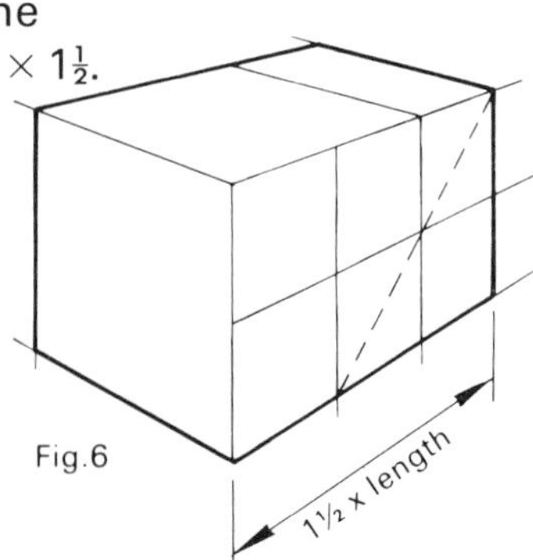

Fig.6

An example using approximate perspective

Drawings of this tape recorder and a camera will be found towards the end of each chapter and are used as further examples of the techniques described.

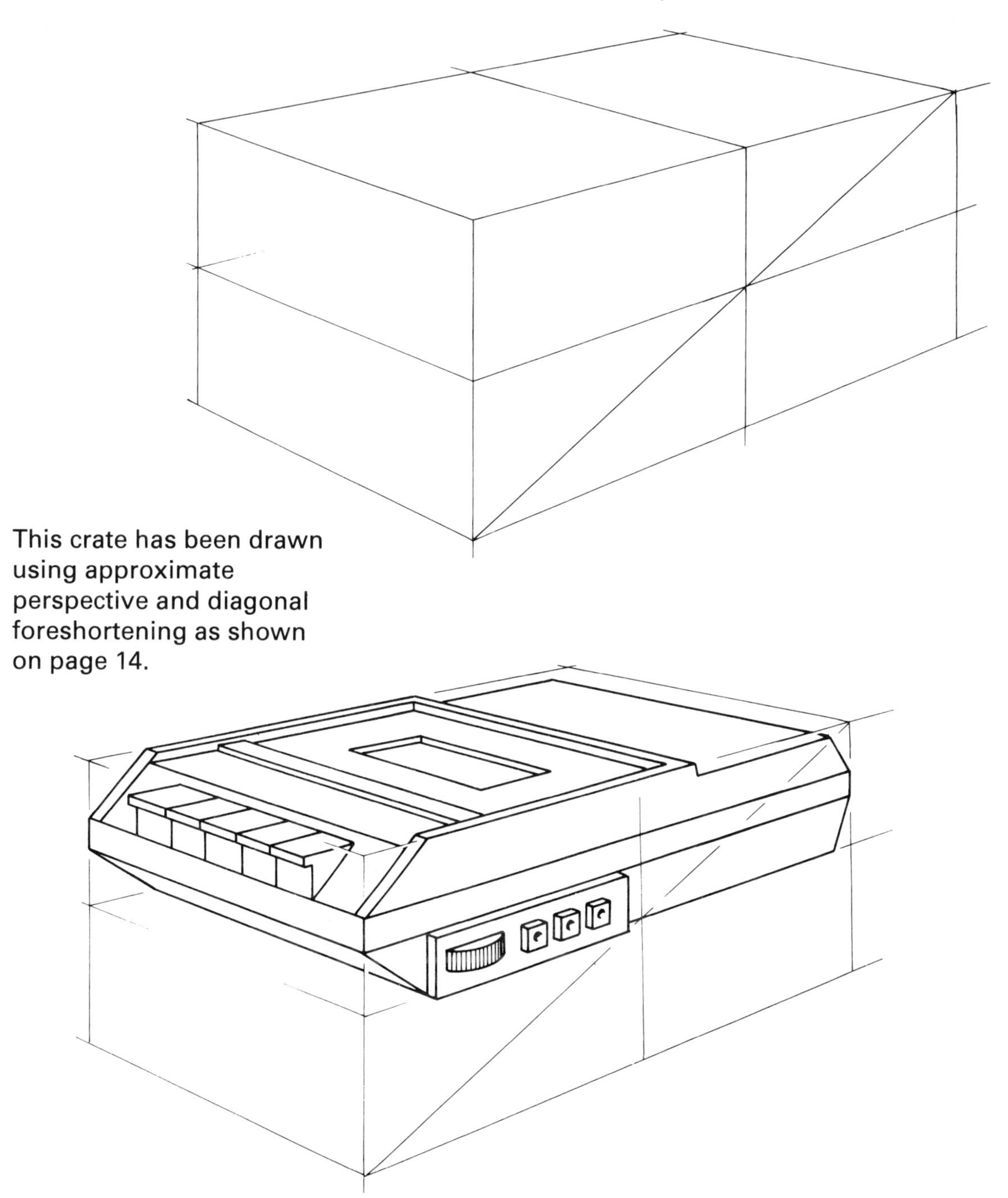

This crate has been drawn using approximate perspective and diagonal foreshortening as shown on page 14.

Exercise 2d

Using approximate perspective and applying your knowledge of building crates from basic cubes, construct a pictorial view of each of the objects below. Draw freehand or with a straight edge and make the nearest vertical edge of your first cube about 50 mm high in each case. All measurements are in millimetres.

1 Dog kennel

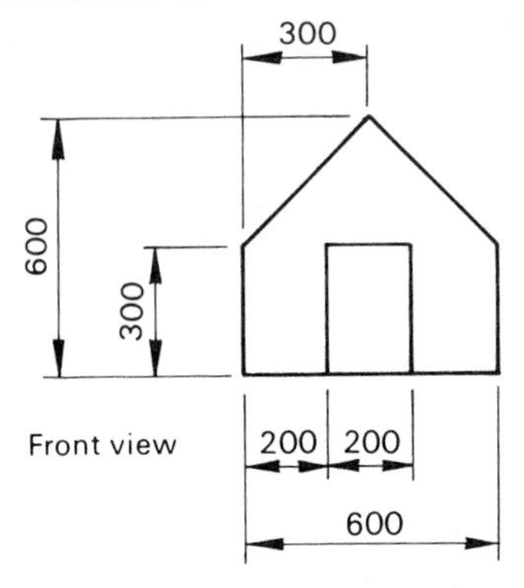

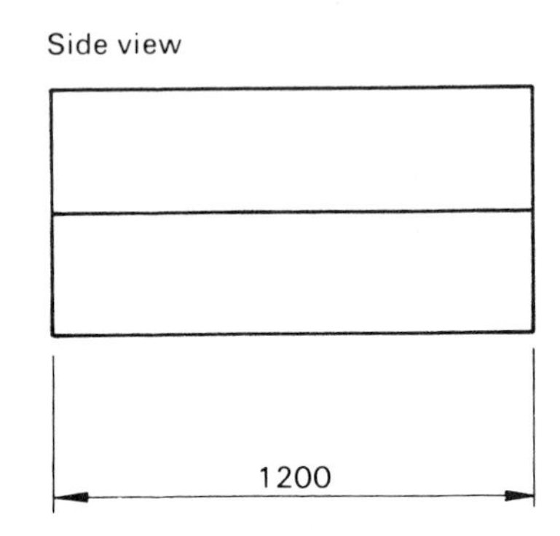

2 Bird box

(made from wood, 15 mm thick)

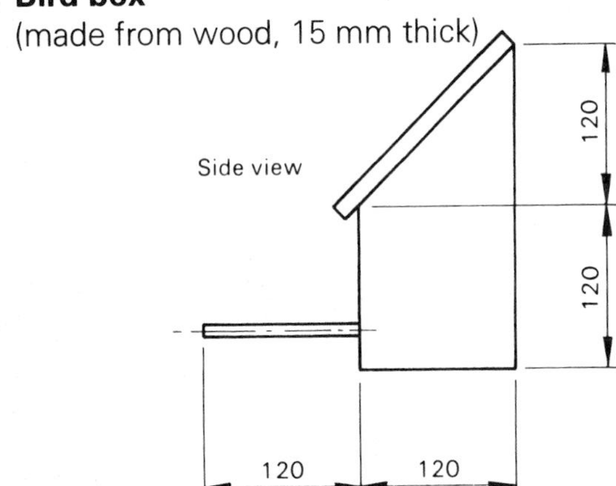

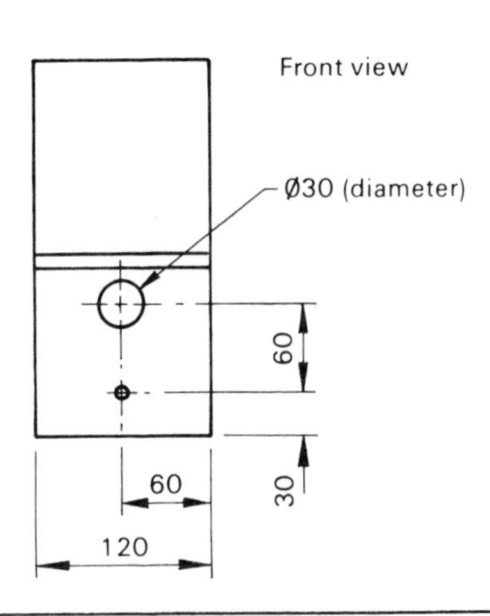

3 A stool with a padded top and a shelf

(made from wood, 20 mm thick)

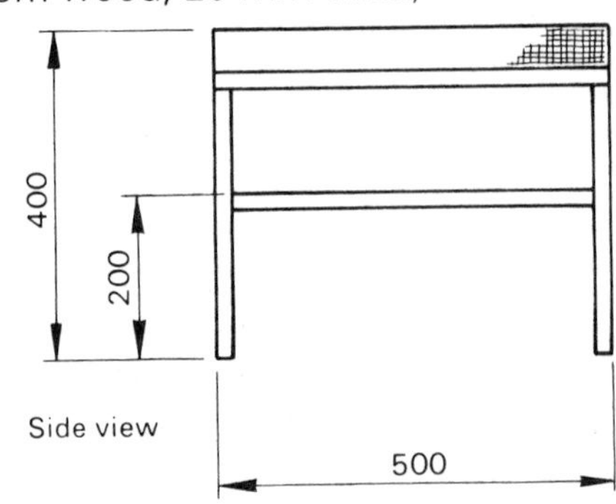

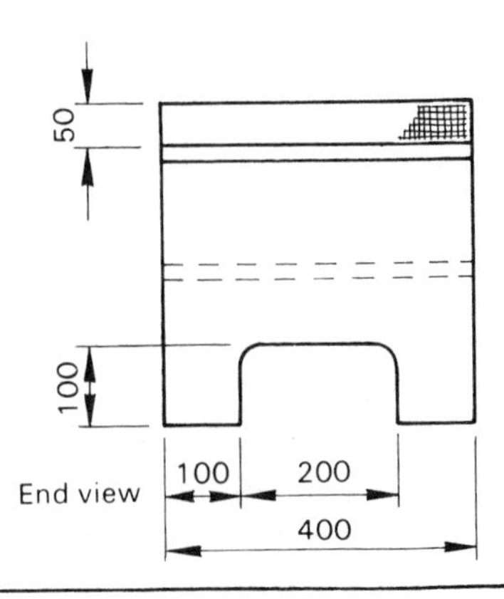

3 The circle in perspective

In Chapter 2 we saw that one effect of perspective is to make lengths which are set at an angle to our line of vision appear shorter than they really are. This photograph of bicycles shows what happens to circles when they are set at angles to our line of vision. The circles are also foreshortened and appear oval, the nearest geometric shape to this being an ellipse. When sketching foreshortened circles, we treat them as ellipses.

The proportions of an ellipse depend on the position from which it is viewed. For example, the middle bicycle of the three on the left-hand side of the photograph has its front wheel leaning towards the viewer and consequently is a very slender ellipse. The wheels of the bicycles on the right-hand side appear as very wide ellipses because they are almost at right angles to the viewer. The wheels on the next page show how the proportions of an ellipse can change.

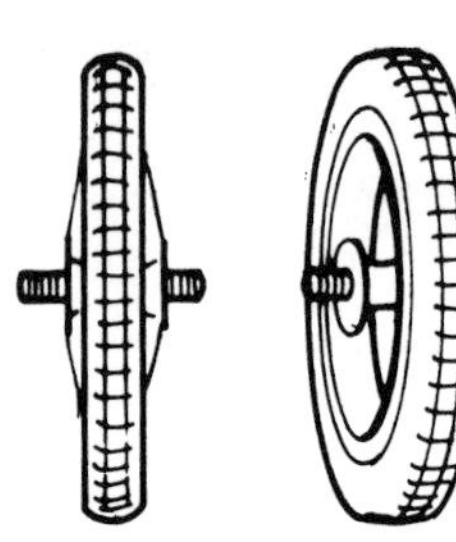

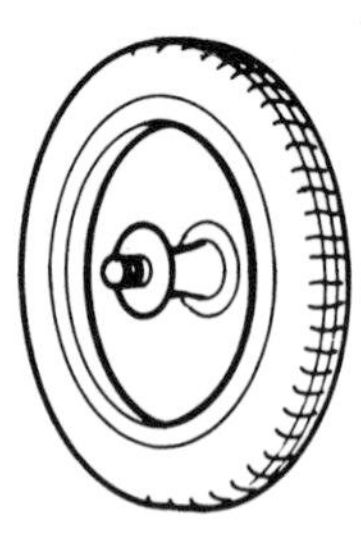
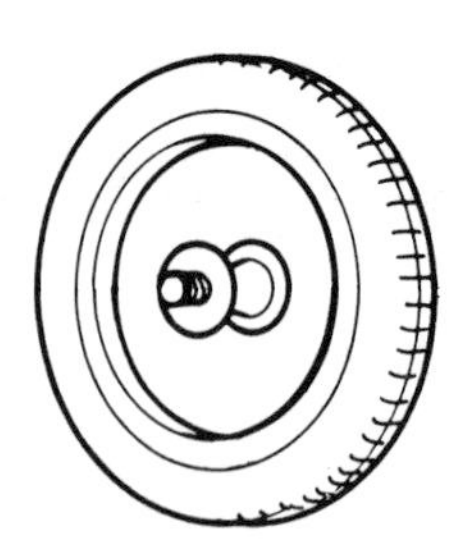
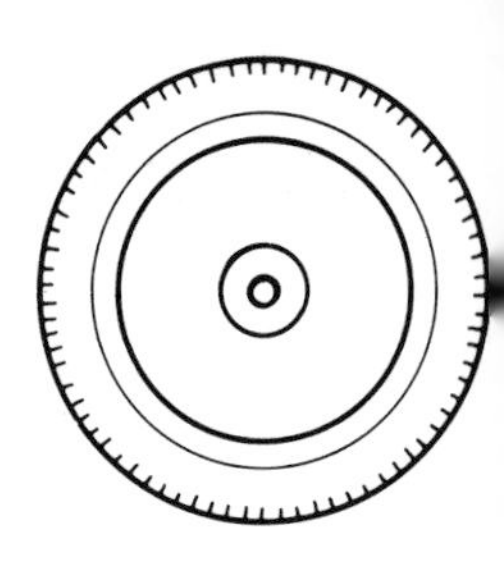

These drawings show how the proportions of an ellipse change. A wheel can be rotated from an end view, where circles are seen as straight lines, to a view directly on to the face of the wheel, where the circles are seen as true shapes. In between these two extremes the ellipses change in their proportions from narrow to wide.

A circle will fit exactly inside a square if its diameter is equal to the length of the side of the square.

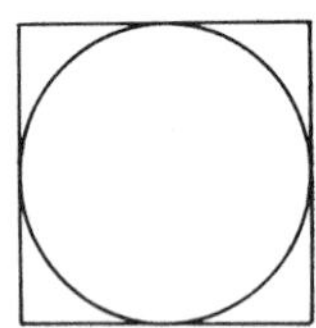

Therefore it follows that an ellipse will fit inside a square drawn in perspective, and also that a square in perspective can be drawn around an ellipse. The two shapes will touch each other in four places.

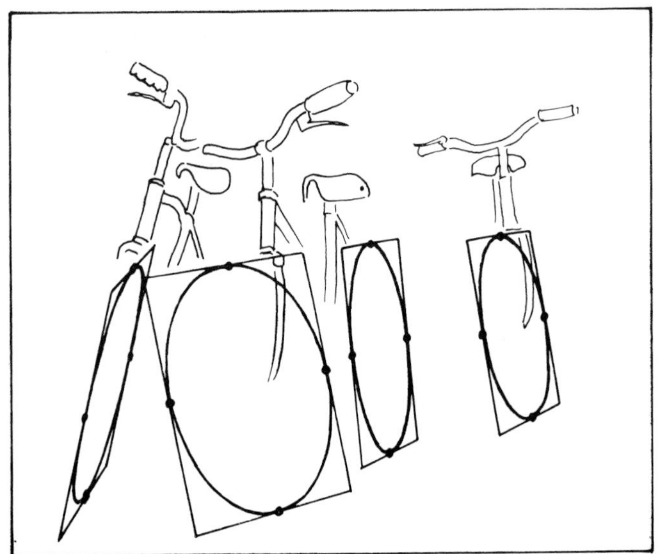

In this drawing, taken from the picture above, you can see the four points of contact, each of which lies in the 'perspective middle' of each side.
Because of foreshortening in a perspective view, the 'half' of the side nearest the viewer will be slightly longer than the 'half' farthest away.

Sketching ellipses

Since each ellipse can be contained in a square drawn in perspective, if we draw the perspective square first we will be able to fit the ellipse inside it.

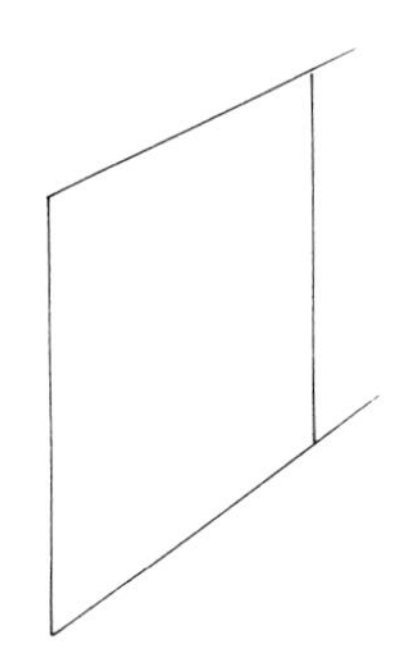

1 Draw the square in perspective.

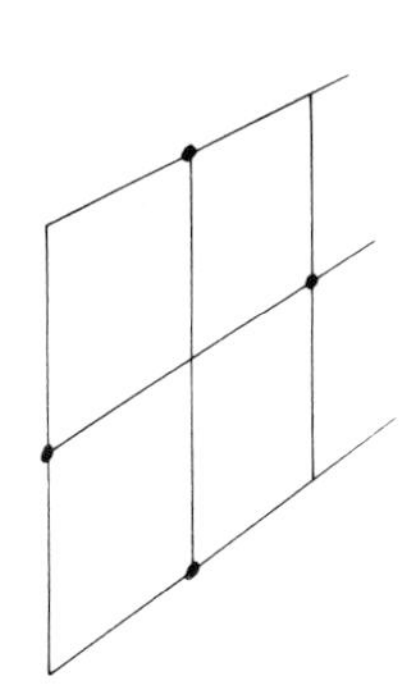

2 Bearing in mind foreshortening, mark in the four points of contact.

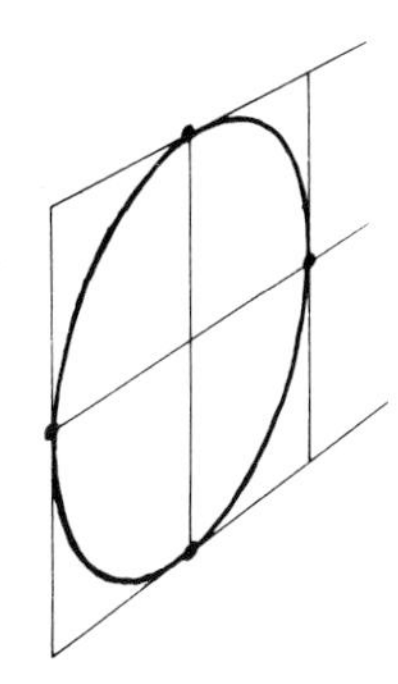

3 Sketch the ellipse.

You must bear in mind that the curves of an ellipse blend together and are not pointed or blunt.

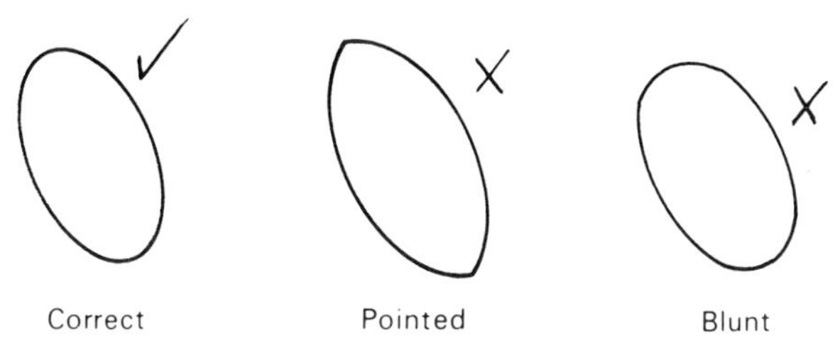

Here is an example showing ellipses sketched within perspective squares.

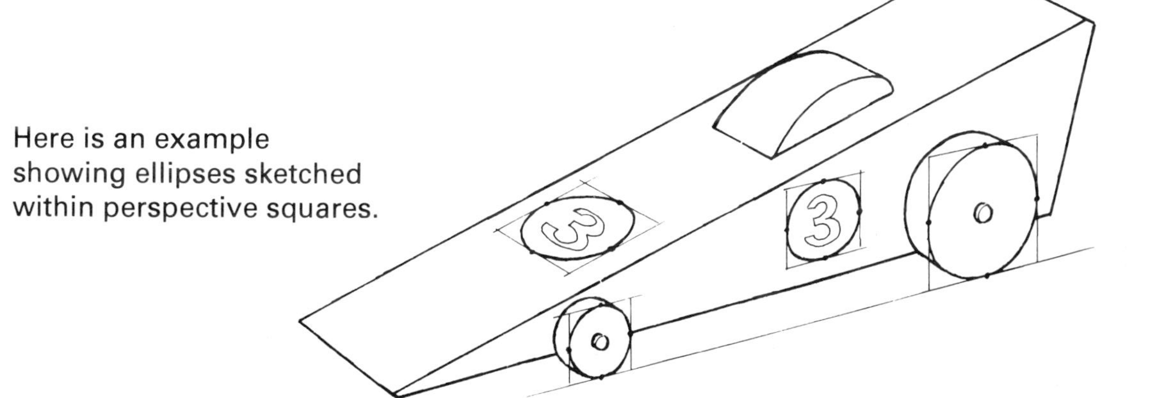

Exercise 3a

Using this picture as a guide, add a plank to four pram wheels to make a simple trolley. Change the view of the wheels if you wish but sketch each wheel within a perspective square as shown on the previous page.

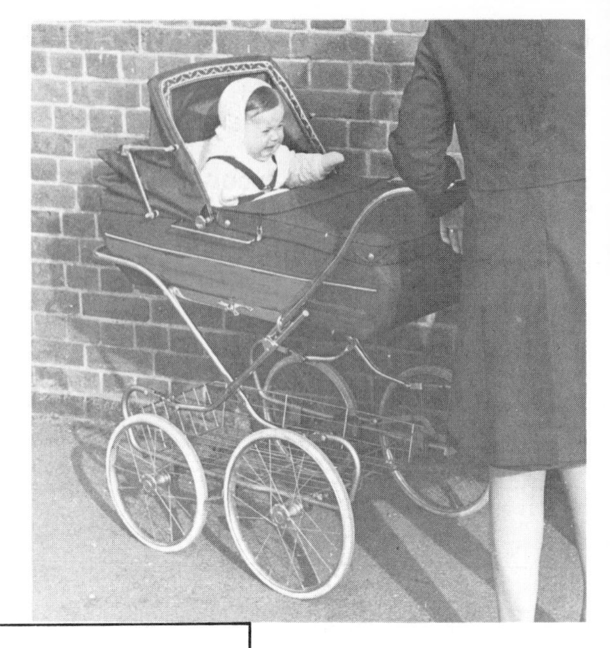

Sketching ellipses using axes

Any true ellipse has two main axes. These are called the **major axis** and the **minor axis**. The major axis is the line that can be drawn across the longest part of the ellipse and through its centre. The minor axis is the line that can be drawn across the narrowest part of the ellipse and through its centre. These two axes are always at right angles to each other.

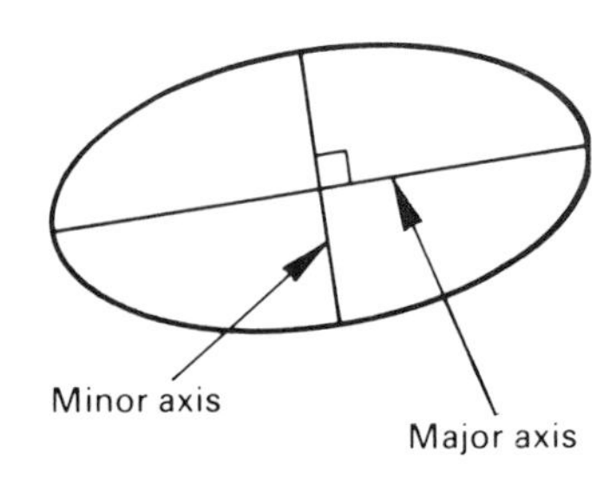

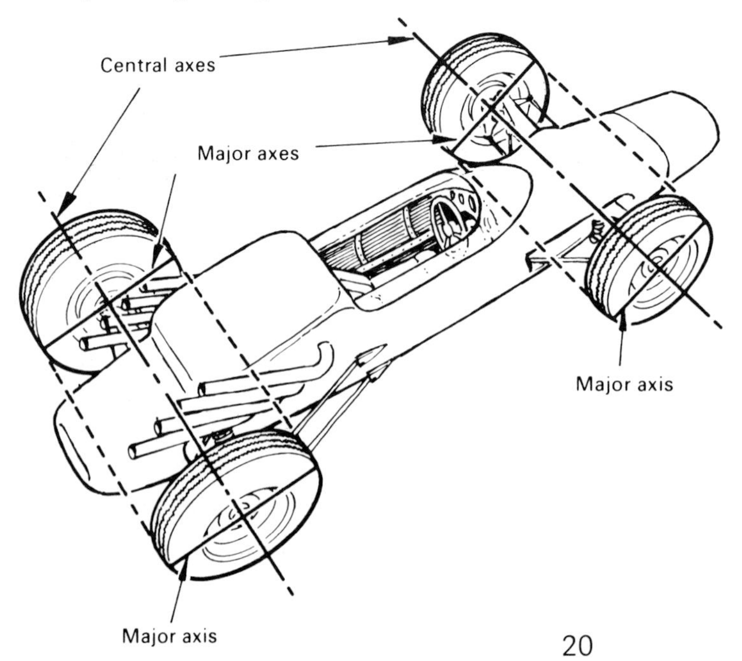

In this drawing of a racing car, the wheels can be taken as the ends of dotted cylinders. The central axis of each cylinder and the major axis of each wheel ellipse are shown. You can see that each major axis is at right angles to a central axis.

Since we know that in an ellipse the major and minor axes are at right angles to each other, then obviously the central and minor axes coincide. We can use axes to help us sketch better ellipses.

If an ellipse is considered as part of a cylinder it is easier to find its major axis. To find the position of the major axis determine the central axis of the cylinder and then draw lines at right angles to this axis. Here are some examples showing the central and major axes in each case.

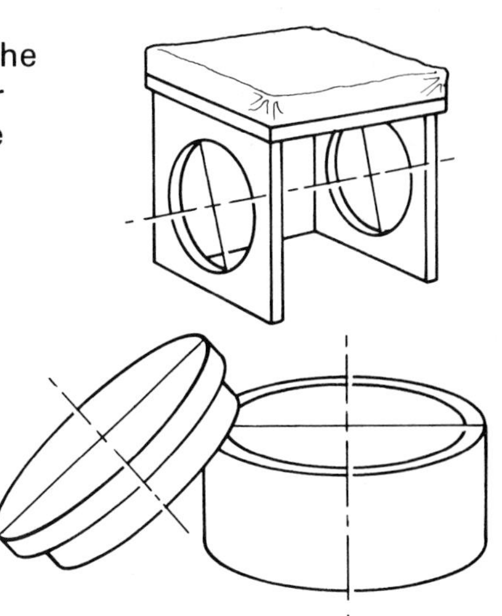

Exercise 3b

In suitable magazines find and trace pictures of six objects which contain ellipses, identifying the central axis and the major axis in each case. Examples that may be useful are advertisements which show cups, glasses, bottles, cameras, and cars, etc.

Ellipse proportions

For any series of ellipses on one central axis, those nearest to the observer will be narrower than those farther away.
On the drawing below, which has been traced from the photograph, you can see that the ellipses on the barrel nearest to the photographer are narrower than those on the other barrel which is on the same central axis.

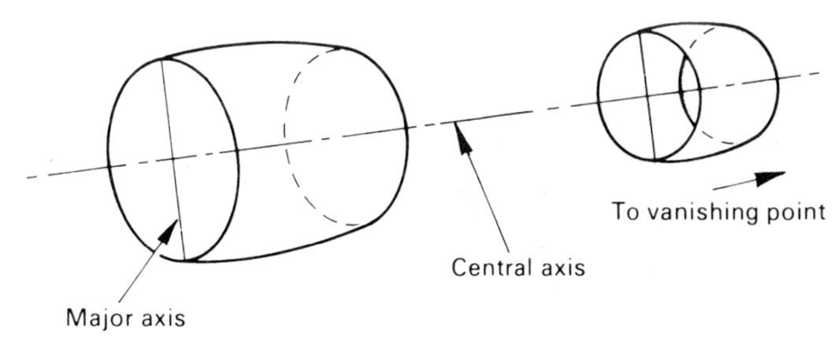

These drawings show how ellipses on a single central axis widen the farther they are from the observer. On the wooden figure the lower they are the wider they become. On the crankshaft, they get wider towards the left-hand side since that end is farthest from the eye.

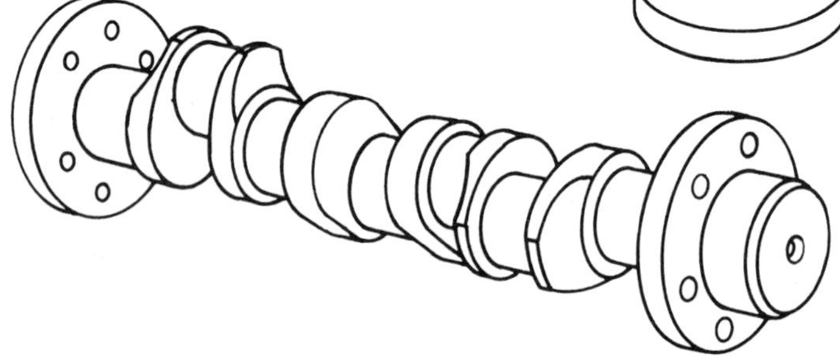

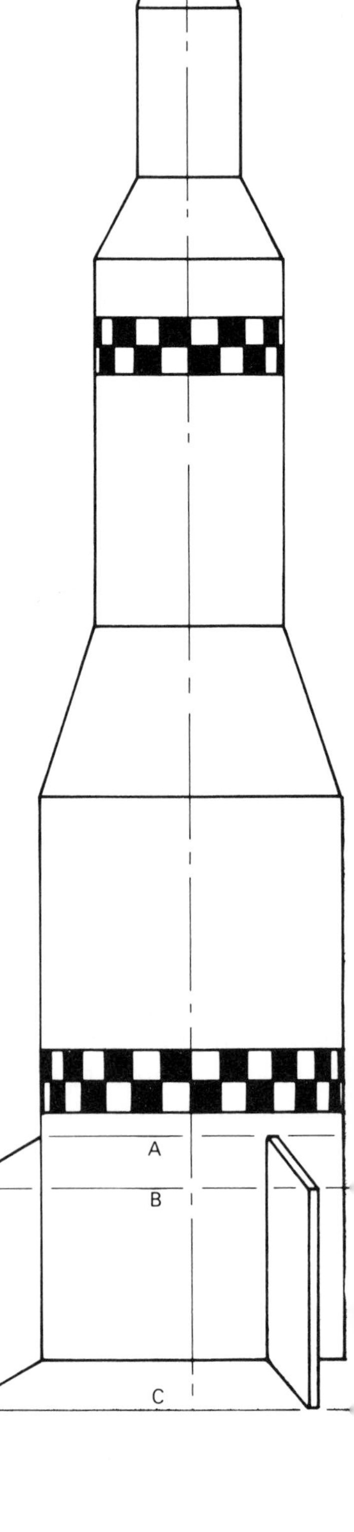

Exercise 3c

Trace this drawing of the rocket and use it as the basis for a view looking on the nose cone. As shown in the sketch below, use the horizontal lines on your tracing as the major axes of ellipses which become progressively wider towards the rear end. Note that the perspective position of the tail fins can also be found by sketching ellipses at levels A, B, and C.

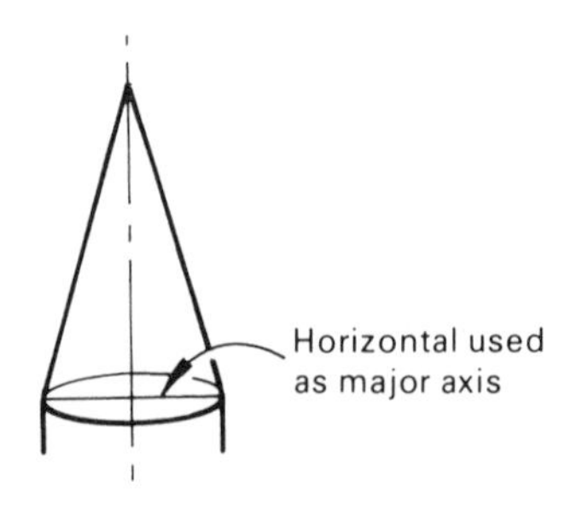

Ellipse templates

To draw ellipses accurately is a skill which can be developed through practice. However, when speed is required, ellipse templates can be used.
We have seen how the proportions of an ellipse can vary with the relative position of the viewer. Ellipse templates cater for ellipses ranging in proportion from narrow to wide and in size from large to small. In the photograph below you can see that templates are plastic sheets with a series of elliptical holes. The angle marked on each template refers to the angle between the line of vision of the observer and the plane of the circle that is being observed. Templates are made to suit ellipses viewed at every 5° angle between 15°, which is for quite narrow ellipses, and 60°, for wide ellipses. They can be purchased singly or in sets of ten.
The lines inscribed on the templates give the positions of the major and minor axes for each ellipse. These axes can be correctly positioned with regard to the central axis of a component and the selected ellipse drawn.

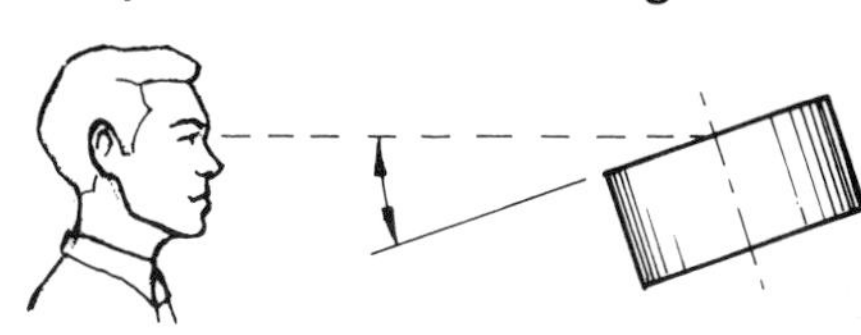

Reference angle marked on ellipse template

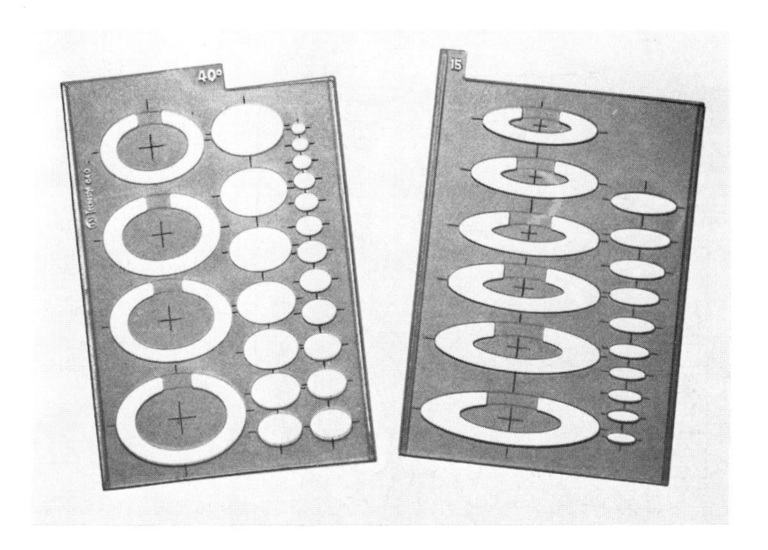

These drawings of common engineering components have been produced using ellipse templates. The thin lines indicate the central axis of each component which is used as a guide for positioning the templates.

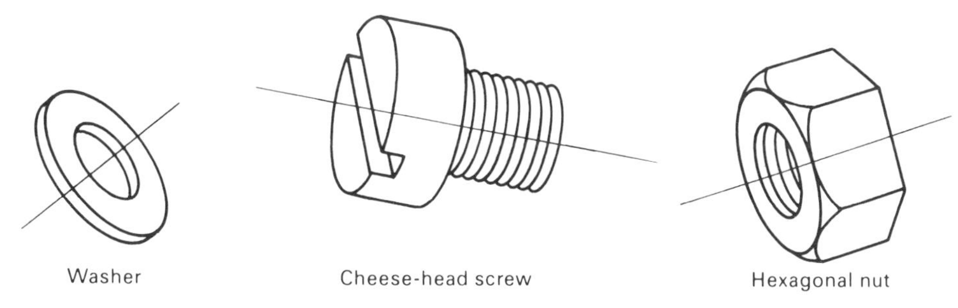

Washer

Cheese-head screw

Hexagonal nut

Examples of illustrations involving ellipses

These drawings demonstrate alternative methods of drawing ellipses to a reasonably accurate standard. The ellipses in the drawing on the right have been sketched by first constructing the central and major axes. The ellipses in the drawing below have been sketched within perspective squares.

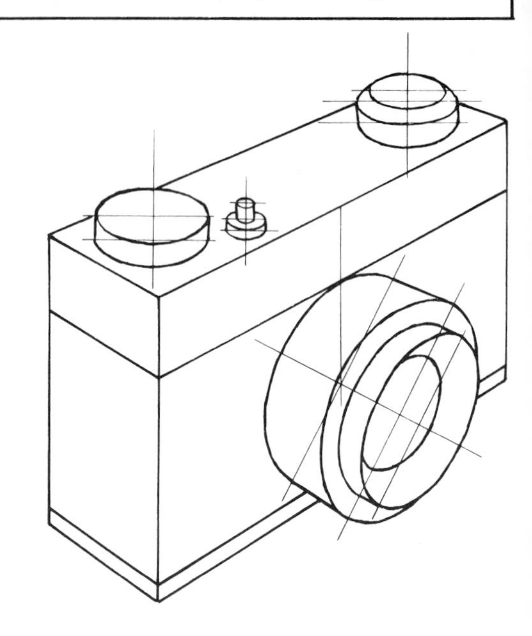

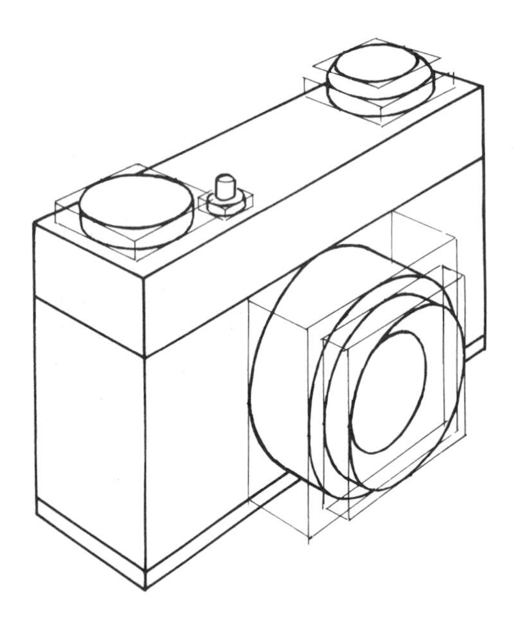

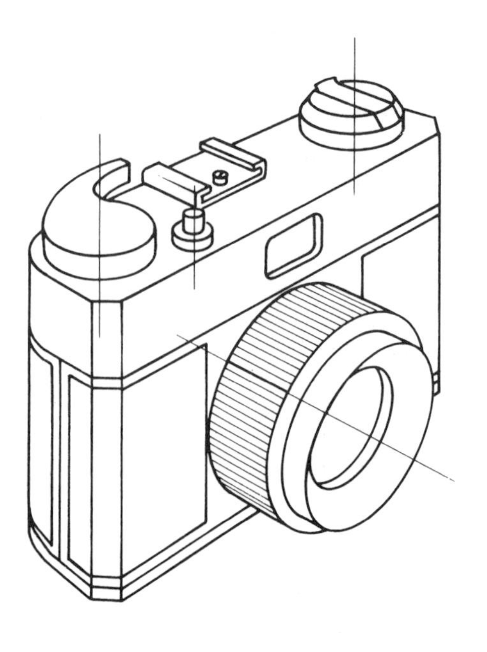

The ellipses on this drawing of the camera have been produced by using an ellipse template.

4 Improving the clarity of line drawings

With the exception of lines that represent pattern or texture, each line on a drawing indicates a change in the direction of a surface or a junction where two surfaces meet.
On this drawing of a short length of square tube each line indicates where two surfaces meet.

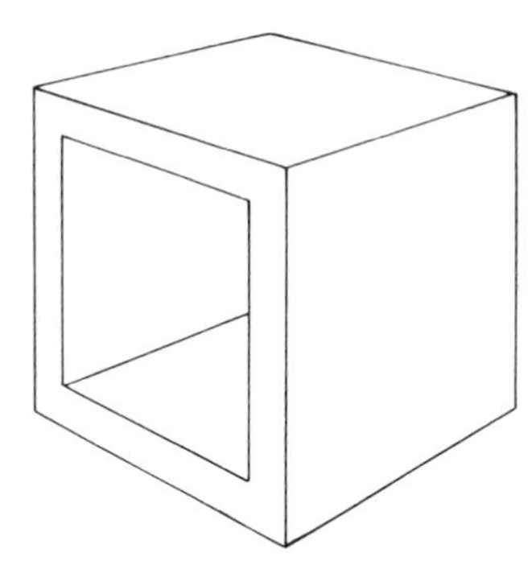

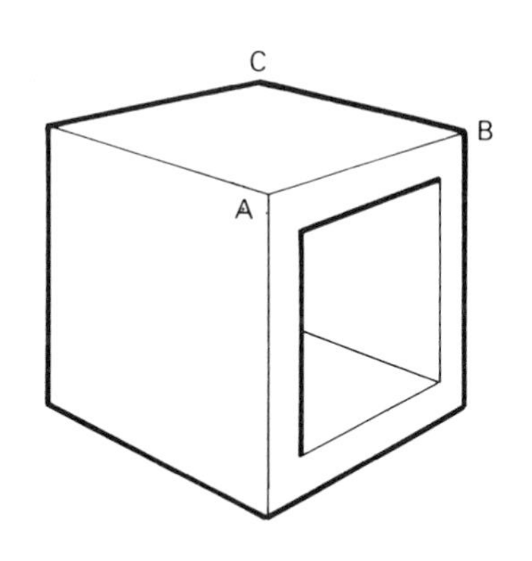

Some lines on this drawing have been thickened to provide variation for the eye and to assist in understanding the form of the object. These thickened lines produce a shadow effect which heightens the impact of the drawing. A rule can be used to help us determine which lines should be thickened. We know that each line represents the junction of two surfaces. At some of these junctions, however, only one of the two surfaces can be seen; edge BC is an example of this. At BC we can only see the top surface since the far side that meets the top is hidden. This line, and other edges where only one surface can be seen, are thickened, whereas edges where both surfaces can be seen meeting, such as line AB, remain thin. The thickened lines should be about twice the thickness of the original lines.

Here are further examples of objects with straight edges showing the application of the thick and thin line technique.

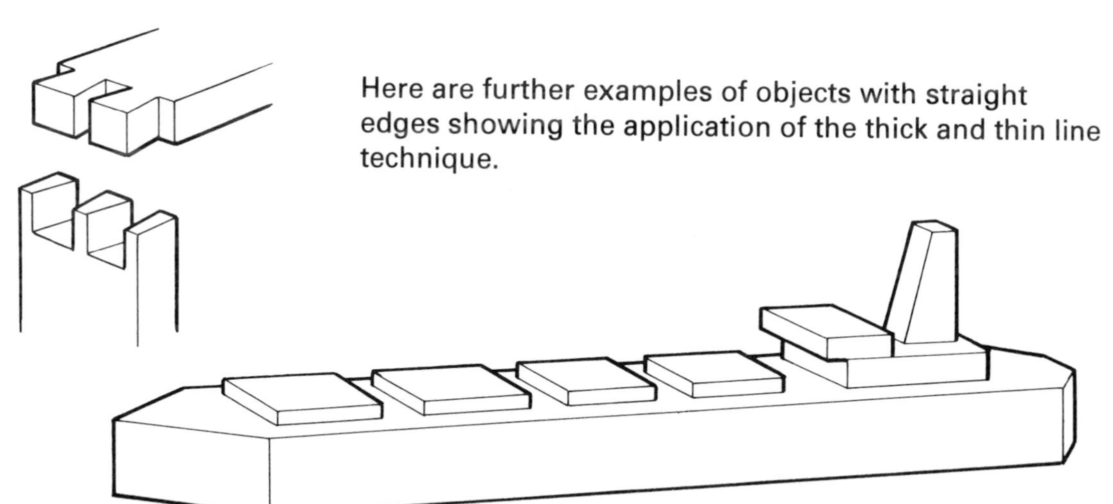

Exercise 4a

Draw these chessmen about twice this size and apply the thick and thin line technique to your drawings. Use whatever aids you have in the way of drawing instruments to produce neat drawings.

Thick and thin lines applied to curved objects

The edge of a curved surface can be treated as the junction of two surfaces: the curved part that can be seen and the curved part that cannot be seen. The line which represents this edge should be thickened.

A hole drawn in perspective becomes an ellipse. When the thick and thin line technique is applied, one side of the ellipse should be thickened whilst the other side remains thin. The change from thin to thick is a gradual tapering of the line thickness.

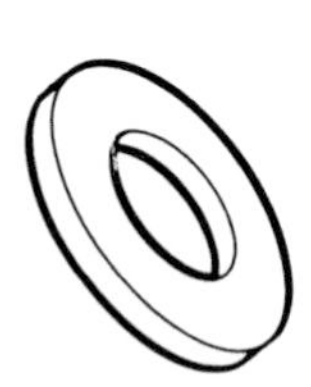

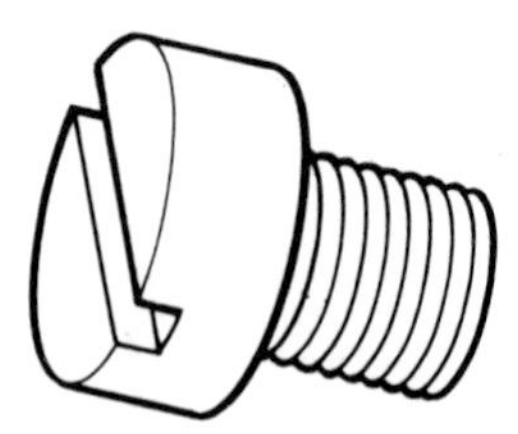

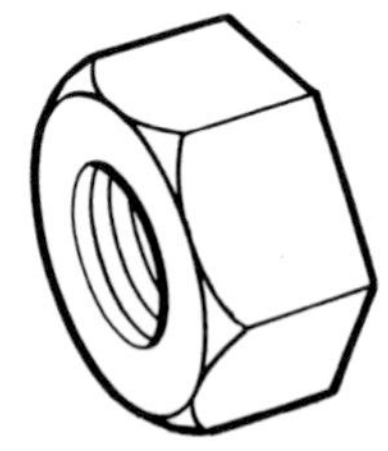

Examples of the thick and thin line technique

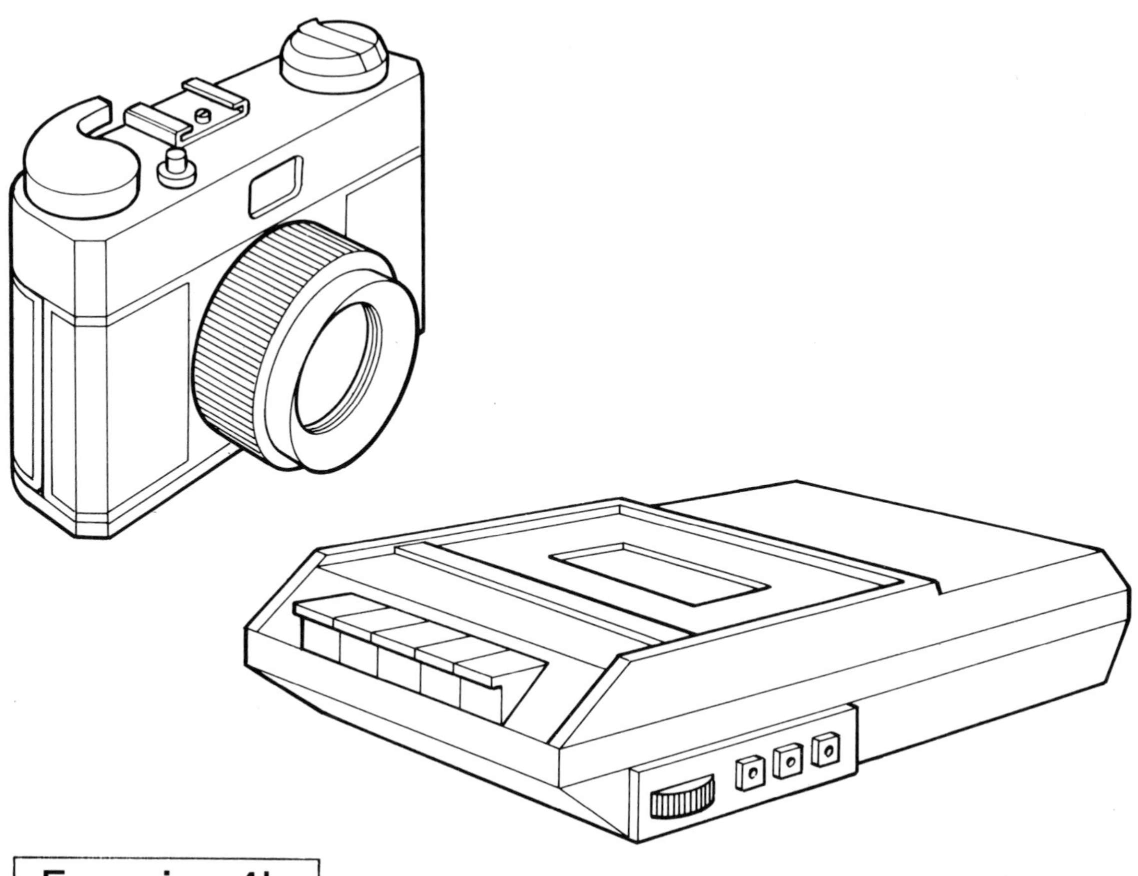

Exercise 4b

Trace this drawing of a torch and apply the thick and thin line technique.

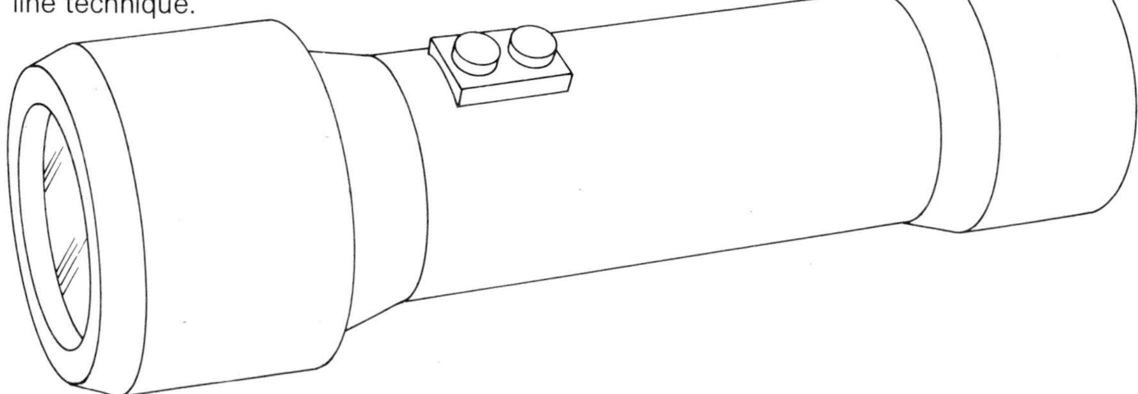

5 Constructing perspective drawings

In our drawings so far we have approximated lines to imaginary vanishing points and estimated the amount of foreshortening involved. This method is quite adequate for conveying the general impression of an article to someone in normal sketching. If a more accurate perspective view is required, which shows the object as it exists, or as it will exist when it is made, then a more formal construction like the one shown in this chapter can be used.

Before we attempt this construction, however, we need to know more about the factors that affect a perspective view since these have to be taken into account in the construction.

There are three main factors which affect a perspective view and in the following sections we will consider each of these in turn:

1 The position of the observer in relation to the object.
2 The distance of the observer from the object.
3 The height of the observer in relation to the object.

The position of the observer

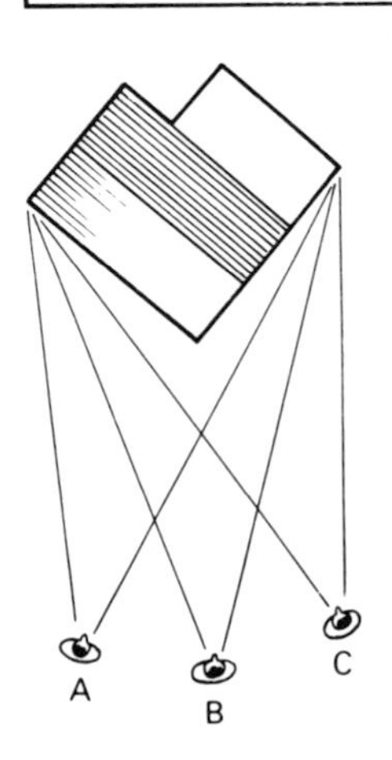

A view looking straight down on something is called a plan; for example, a map is the plan of a country.

The drawing shows a plan view of three men positioned at points A, B, and C looking at a building. The photographs on the right show that each man sees a different view of the building. If you wanted to see the view that the man sees from position B, then obviously you must stand at position B and no other.

The view seen from position A

The view seen from position B

The view seen from position C

The distance of the observer

This series of drawings shows what happens when one moves towards an object. You will note that as the image increases in size, the angles of the lines going to the vanishing points change.

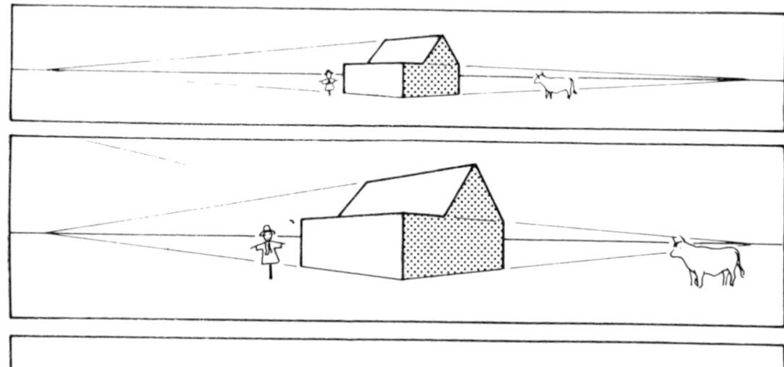

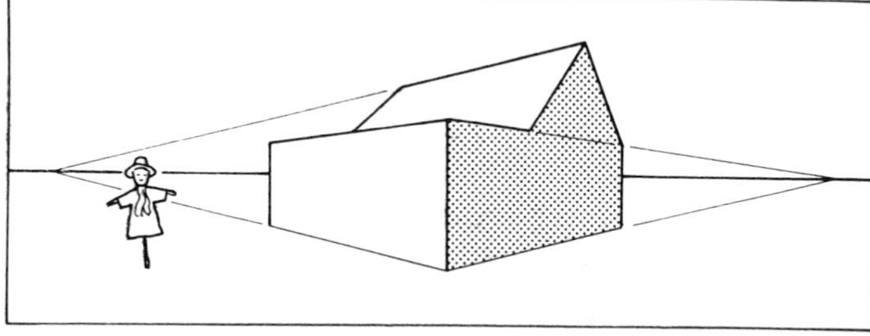

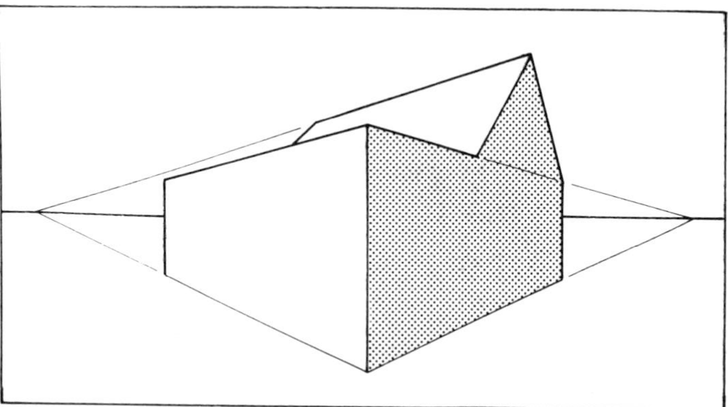

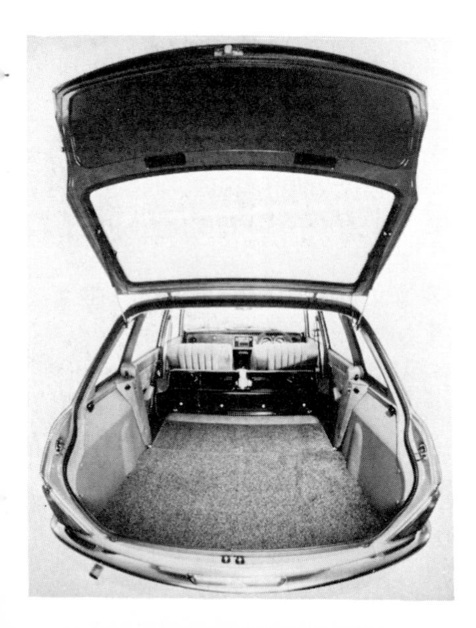

If the position where the viewer is standing is too close to the object, the resulting perspective becomes very distorted. This picture of a car is an example of a distorted view which was achieved by photographing the car through a special lens. Is this picture a one-, two-, or three-point perspective view?

The height of the observer

We have seen that the horizon is the horizontal line between two vanishing points. The position of the horizon changes in accordance with one's eye level, as these examples show.

In this picture the horizon passes through the building as shown.

VP

Horizon

Here, the viewer's eye-level is much lower than in the picture above. The horizon also occurs at this lower level.

In this case the horizon appears higher than in the previous examples since the building is being viewed from a higher position.
You can try this effect for yourself by viewing an object from different heights.

Exercise 5a

With drawings based on this L-shaped arrangement of play boxes, show what view you see of the boxes when:

1 you move to the left of them;
2 you move to the right of them;
3 you move nearer to them;
4 you move farther from them;
5 you climb a ladder to view them;
6 you lie on the ground to view them.

The formal perspective construction

This construction requires the use of drawing instruments. The perspective view which results is more accurate than a sketch. The following pages show the stages in producing a perspective drawing of a simple house.

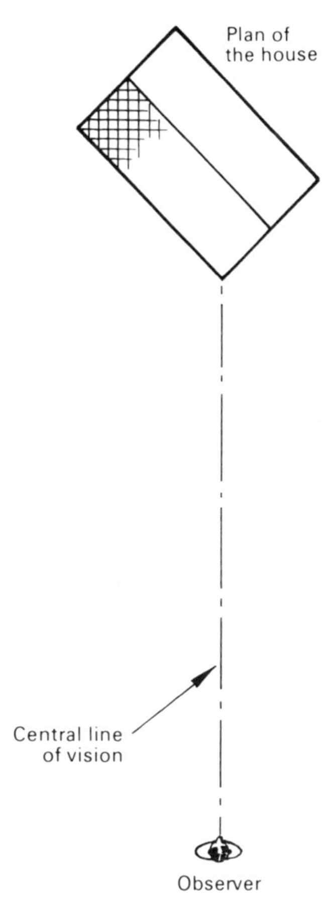

Stage 1

Two of the three main factors that affect a perspective view are decided at this stage: the position of the observer in relation to the object and the distance of the observer from the object.
A plan view of the object, in this case the house, is placed at the required position in relation to the observer (see page 28). The distance between the observer and the house should be neither too small nor too great, either of which might result in poor perspective (see page 29). A useful general rule which can be applied is to position the observer at a distance which is equivalent to three to five times the height of the object. The central line of vision is the line between the observer and the point on the object nearest to him.

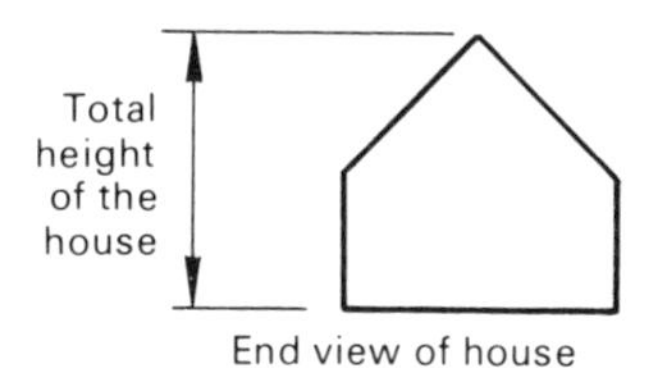

End view of house

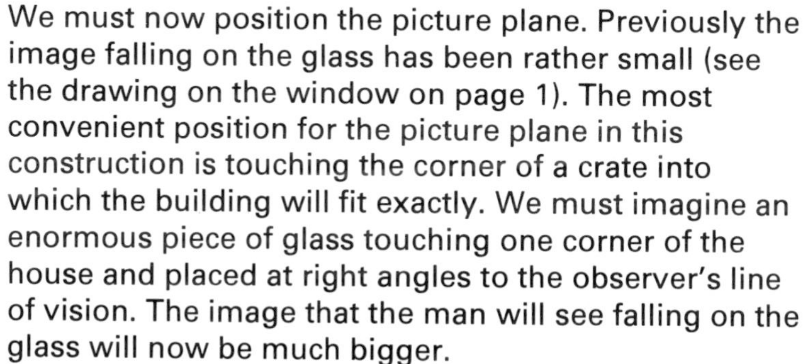

We must now position the picture plane. Previously the image falling on the glass has been rather small (see the drawing on the window on page 1). The most convenient position for the picture plane in this construction is touching the corner of a crate into which the building will fit exactly. We must imagine an enormous piece of glass touching one corner of the house and placed at right angles to the observer's line of vision. The image that the man will see falling on the glass will now be much bigger.

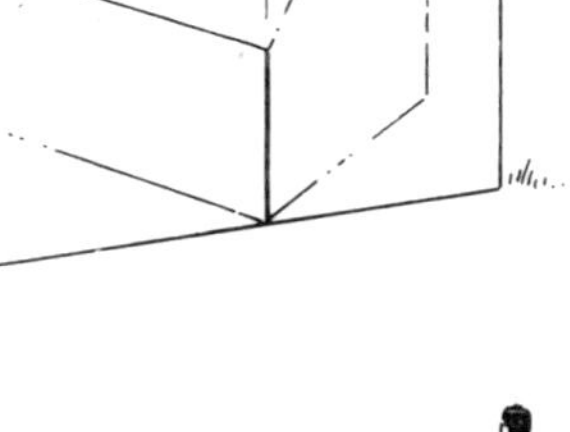

Stage 2

Draw the plan of the picture plane at right angles to the central line of vision and touching the corner of the house nearest to the observer.

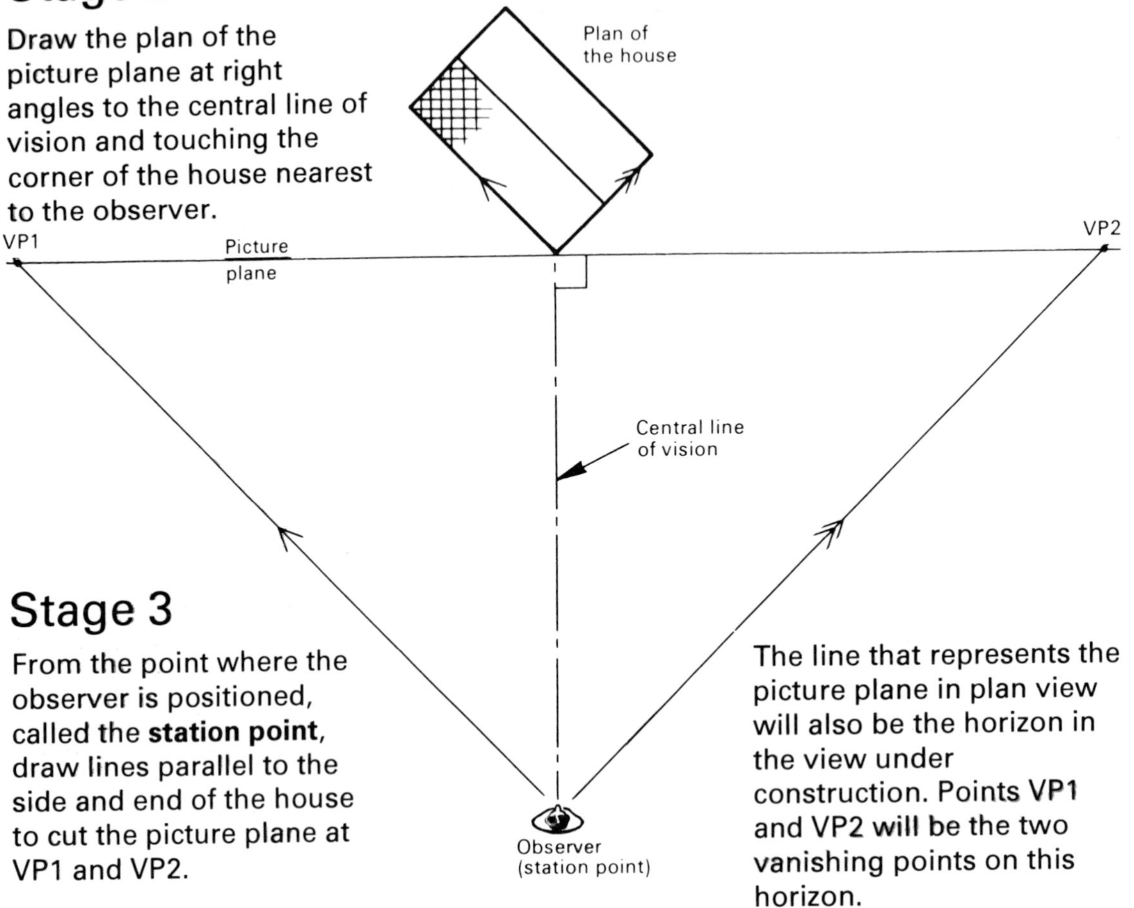

Stage 3

From the point where the observer is positioned, called the **station point**, draw lines parallel to the side and end of the house to cut the picture plane at VP1 and VP2.

The line that represents the picture plane in plan view will also be the horizon in the view under construction. Points VP1 and VP2 will be the two vanishing points on this horizon.

Stage 4

The third factor that affects a perspective view, the height of the observer's eye-level in relation to the object (see page 30), must now be determined. Here you can see that the observer is standing on the same surface as the house and the eye-level is taken as 1.7 metres above the base of the house. Using the same scale as used for the plan, mark point A 1.7 metres below the horizon on the central line of vision. Take lengths AB and AC directly from the end view of the house and mark these to scale as shown.

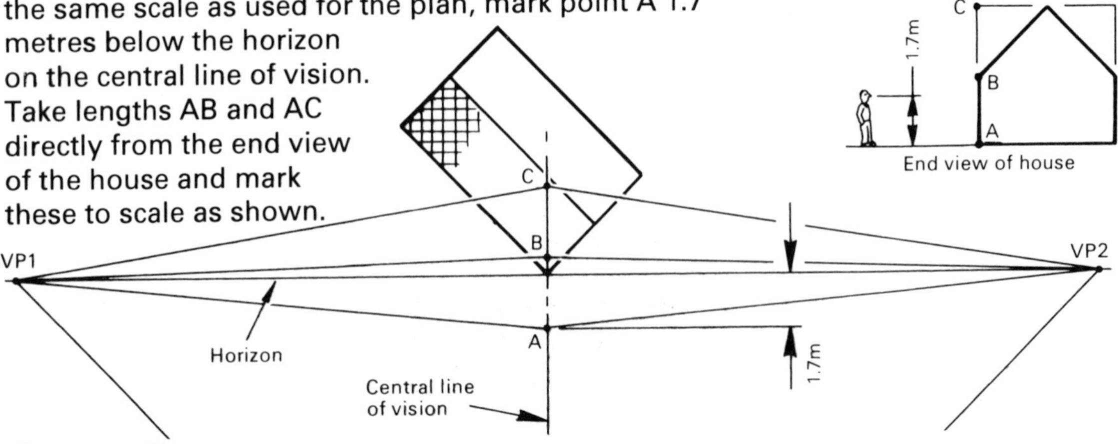

Stage 5

Draw lines from A, B, and C to both vanishing points.

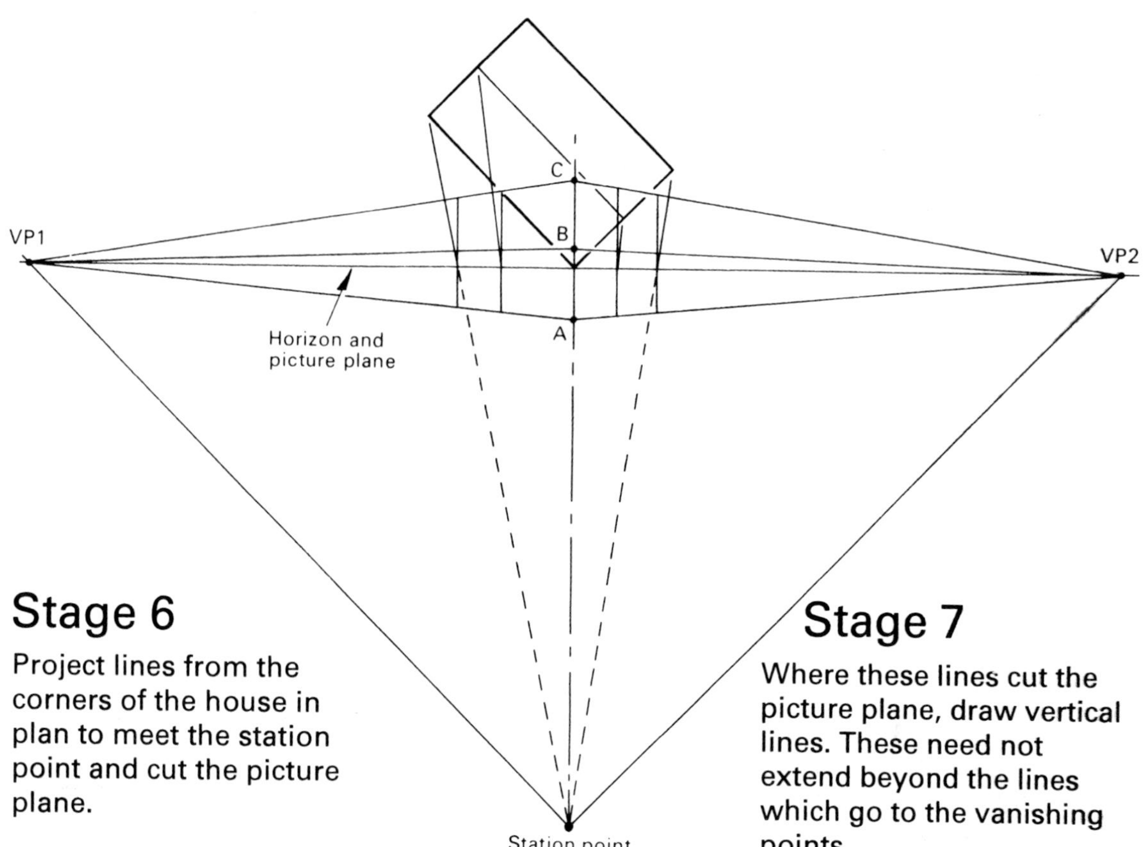

Stage 6

Project lines from the corners of the house in plan to meet the station point and cut the picture plane.

Stage 7

Where these lines cut the picture plane, draw vertical lines. These need not extend beyond the lines which go to the vanishing points.

Stage 8

The drawing can now be completed within this framework of lines.

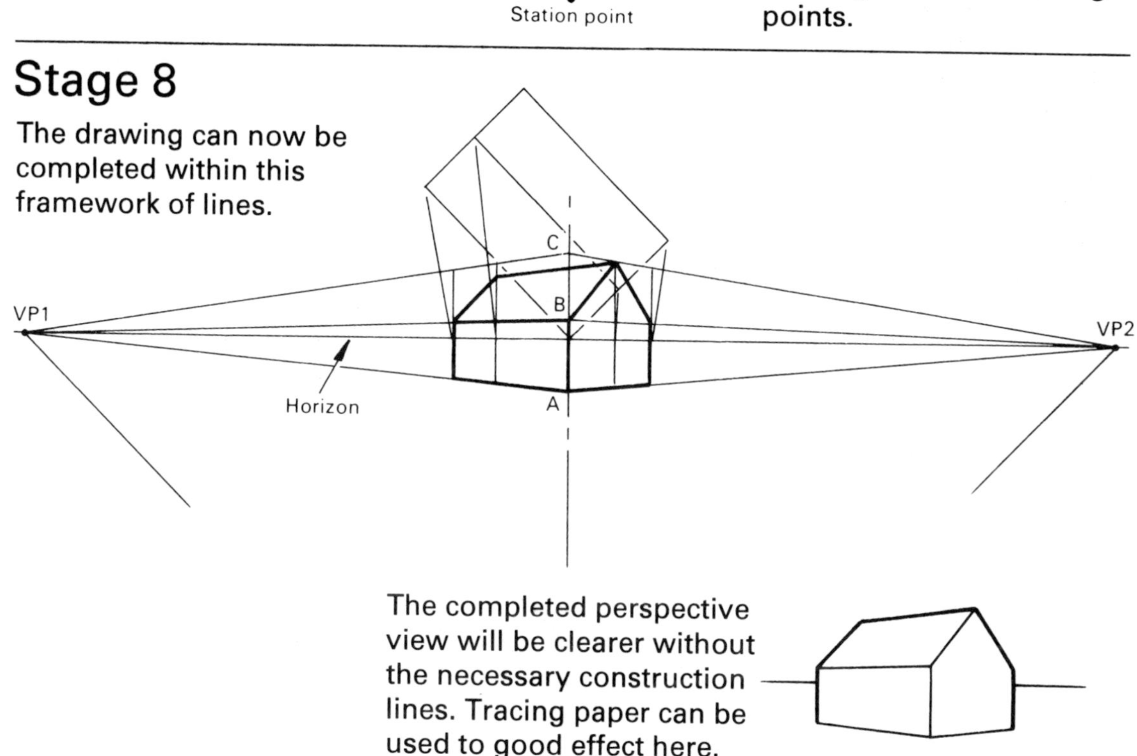

The completed perspective view will be clearer without the necessary construction lines. Tracing paper can be used to good effect here.

Two-point perspective views with false horizons

The only difference between this and the previous construction is that the height of the house, AC, has been moved down the central line of vision. The result is a view looking on top of the house. In reality, this view should have a third vanishing point but, since the amount of tapering is so slight, this has been ignored.

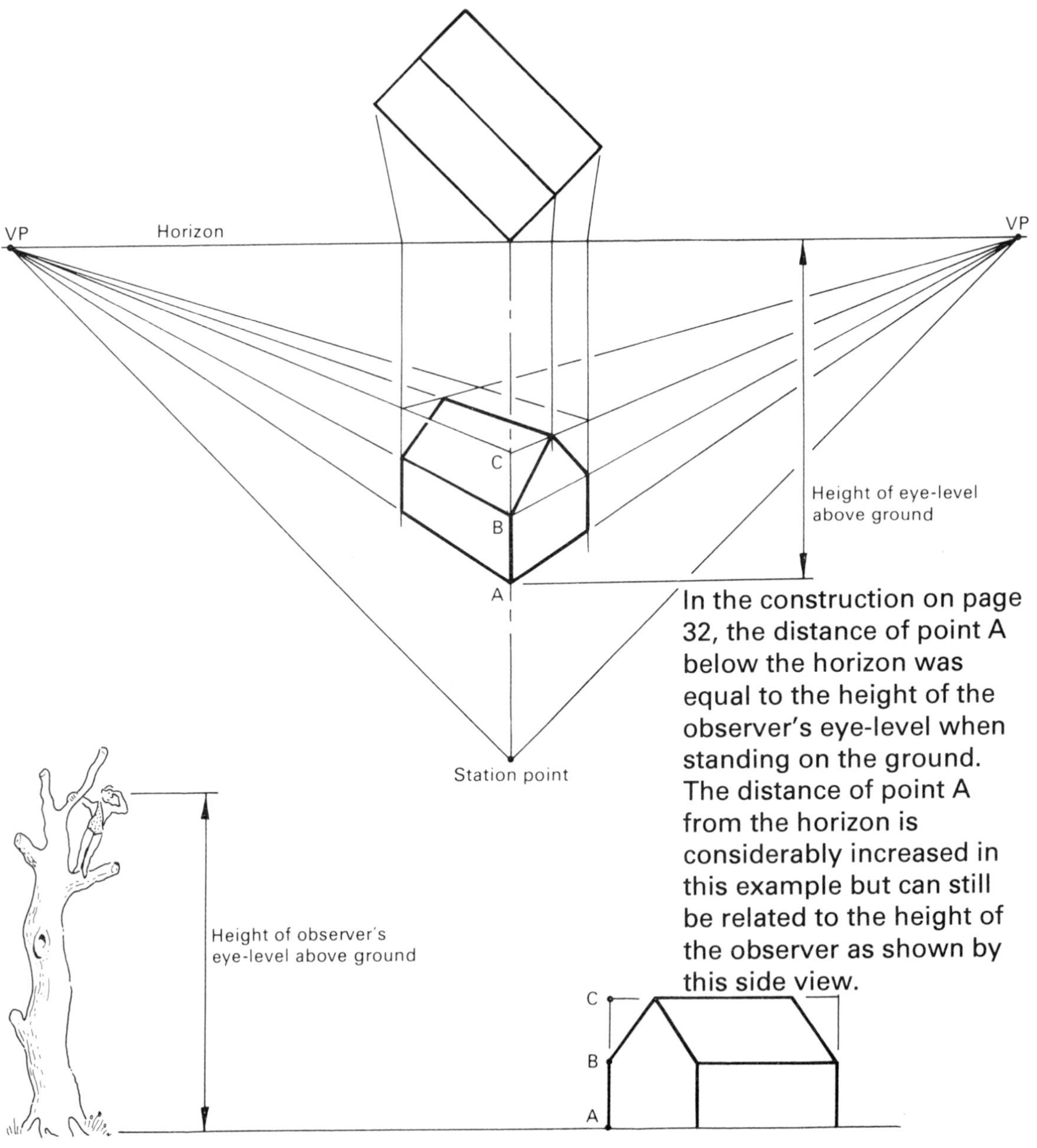

In the construction on page 32, the distance of point A below the horizon was equal to the height of the observer's eye-level when standing on the ground. The distance of point A from the horizon is considerably increased in this example but can still be related to the height of the observer as shown by this side view.

Plotting points within the perspective crate

When this house is placed inside a crate we find that the ends of the upper ridge rest inside the edges of the crate.
The dashed lines drawn on the construction below show how to find where these points occur on the perspective view. There are two methods that can be used, both of which involve projecting each point to be found to the edge of the crate in the plan view, down to the correct level on the perspective crate, and then to vanishing point.
The method shown at the left-hand side of the perspective view requires points plotted on two edges of the crate. In the alternative method at the right-hand side only one point is projected down to the edge of the crate.
To plot points on any perspective view which occurs inside the crate, one of these two methods must be used.

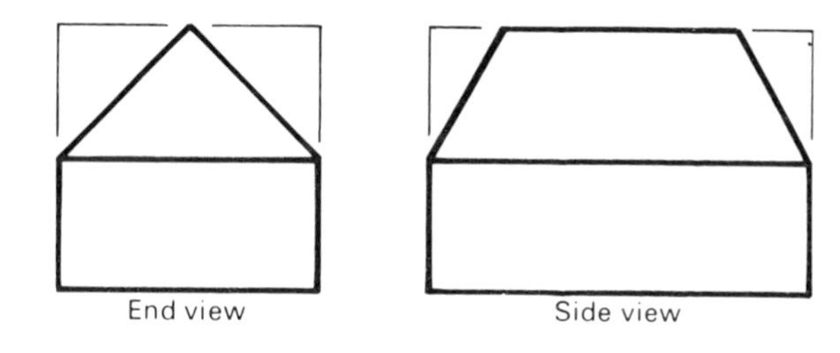

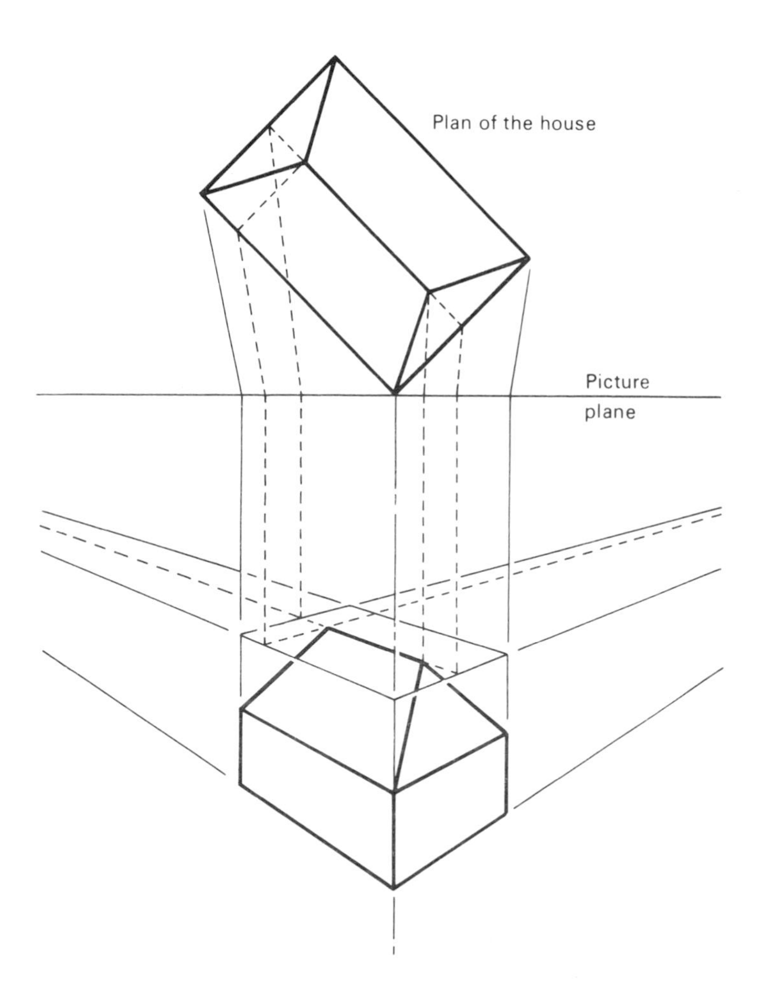

Exercise 5b

Construct a two-point perspective view of each of these houses from the information given. Each construction will fit on A3 size paper used horizontally.

1 The station point is 150 mm from the picture plane.
The eye-level is 15 mm above the base of the house.
Follow the stages as laid out on pages 31 to 33 and remember to construct the crate which would contain the house first.

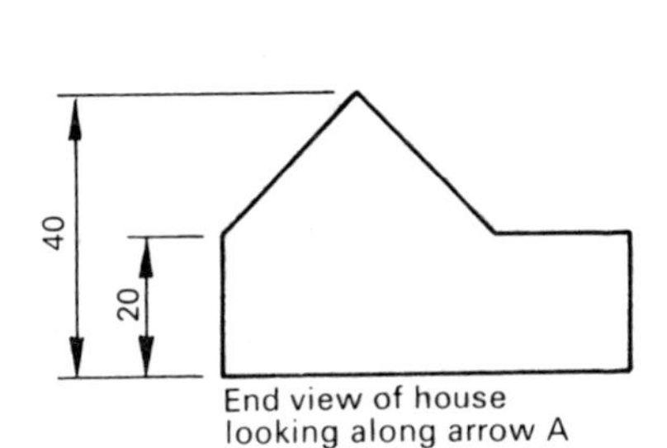

End view of house looking along arrow A

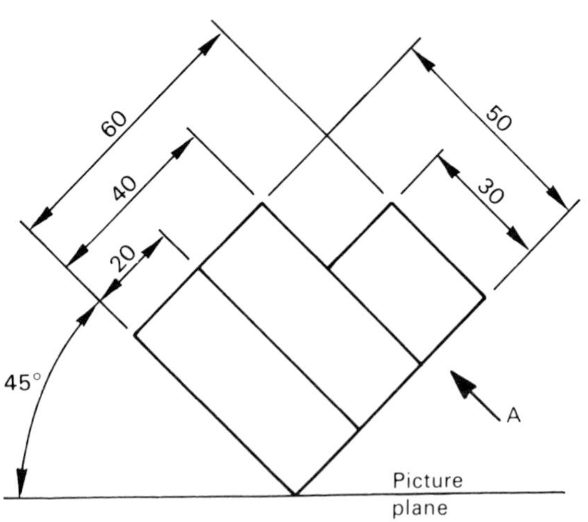

2 The station point is 160 mm from the picture plane.
The eye-level is 80 mm above the base of the house.
See page 34 for a similar situation to this example.
Note that the sides of the house make angles of 30° and 60° with the picture plane.

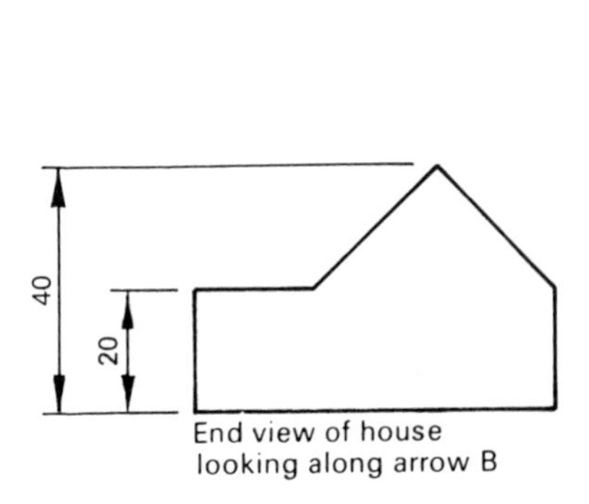

End view of house looking along arrow B

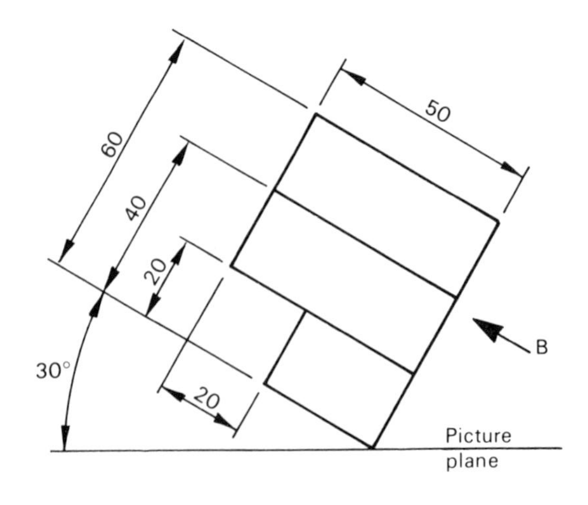

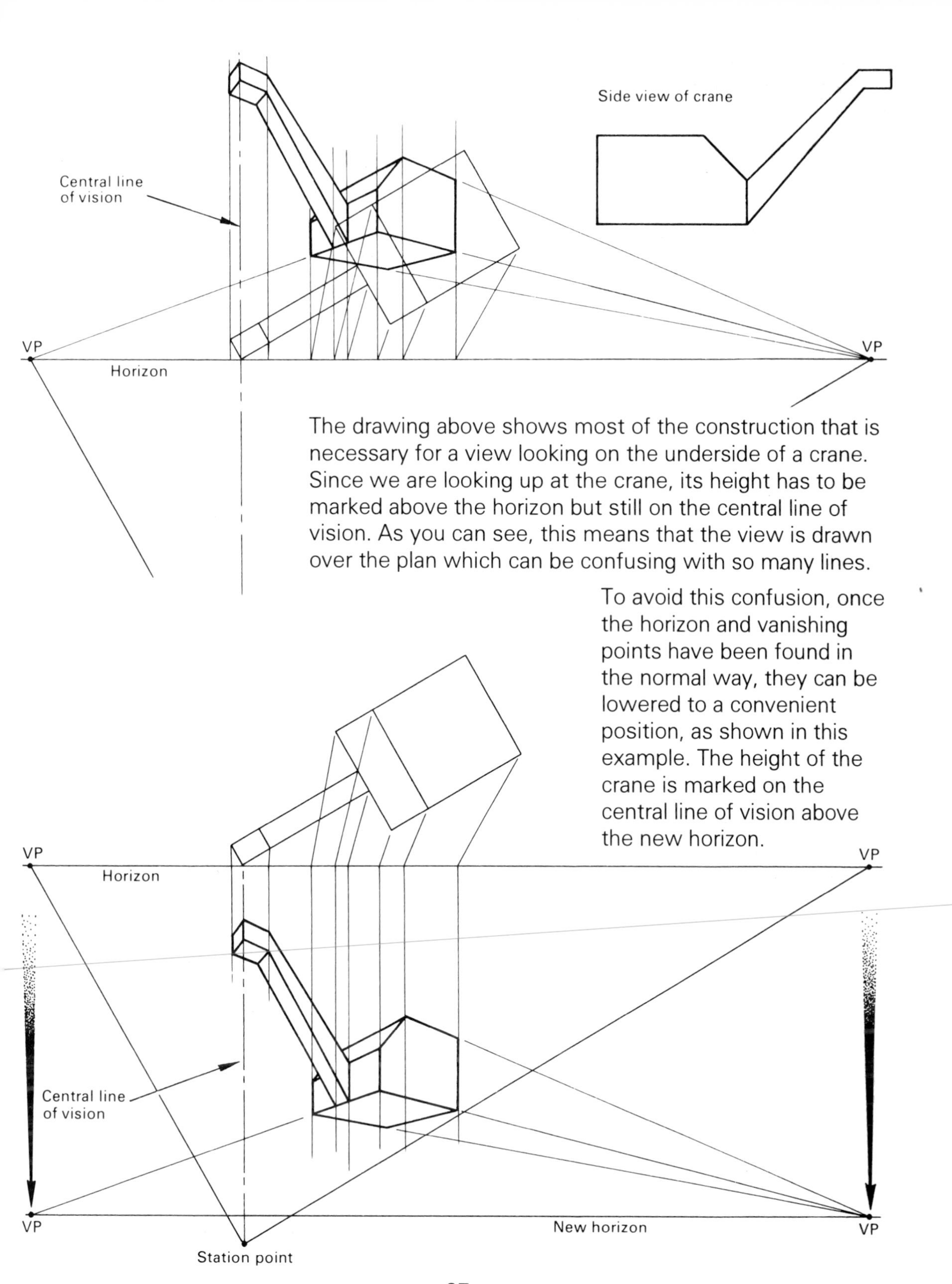

The drawing above shows most of the construction that is necessary for a view looking on the underside of a crane. Since we are looking up at the crane, its height has to be marked above the horizon but still on the central line of vision. As you can see, this means that the view is drawn over the plan which can be confusing with so many lines.

To avoid this confusion, once the horizon and vanishing points have been found in the normal way, they can be lowered to a convenient position, as shown in this example. The height of the crane is marked on the central line of vision above the new horizon.

Two-point perspective drawing of a tape recorder

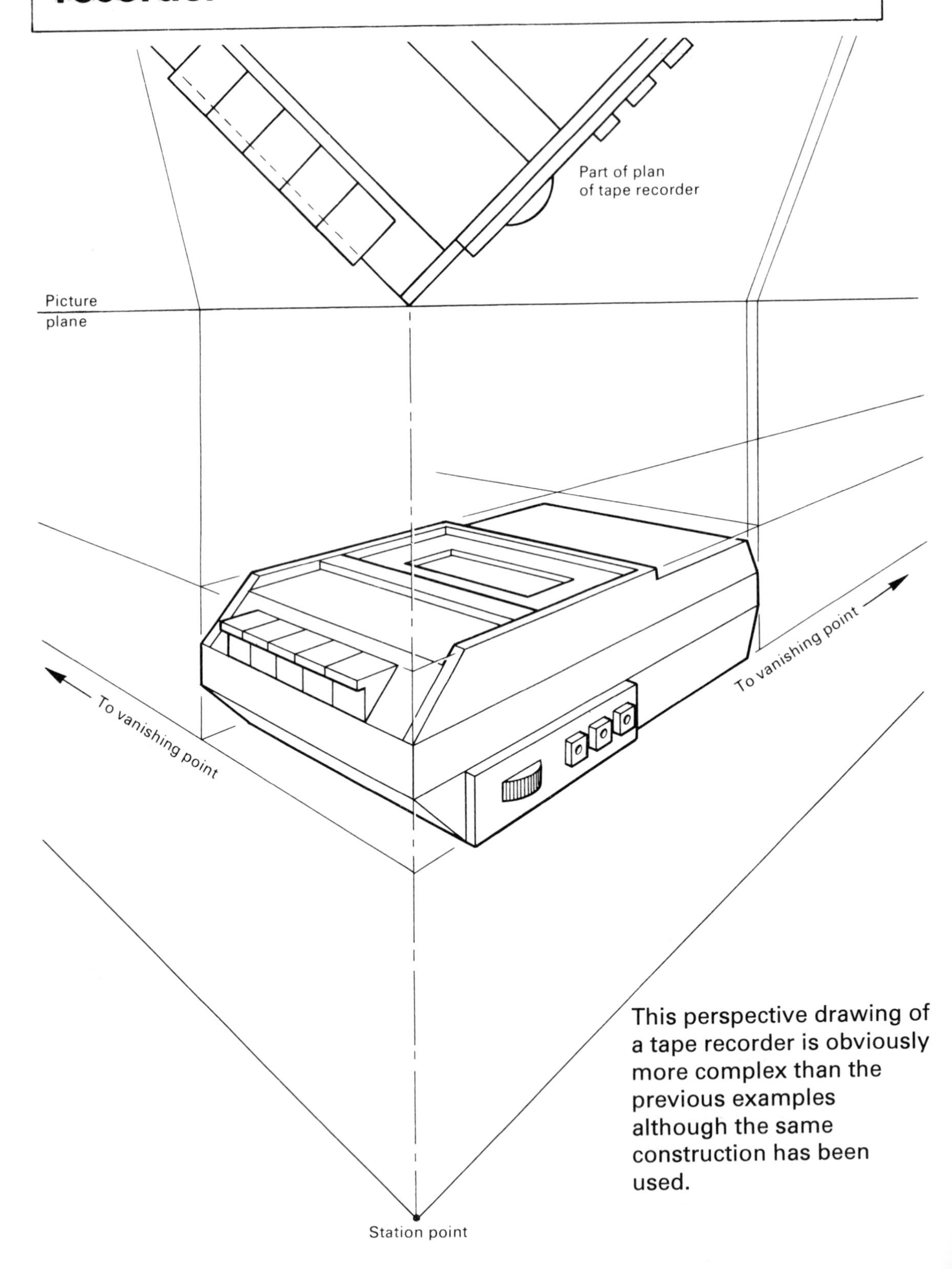

This perspective drawing of a tape recorder is obviously more complex than the previous examples although the same construction has been used.

Exercise 5c

1 Construct a two-point perspective view of this house, with the station point 150 mm from the picture plane and the eye level 15 mm above the base of the house. After completing the usual construction as far as finding the vanishing points, move the horizon to a more convenient position (as shown on page 37).

Construct two crates in this case, one to contain the garage and the other the house.

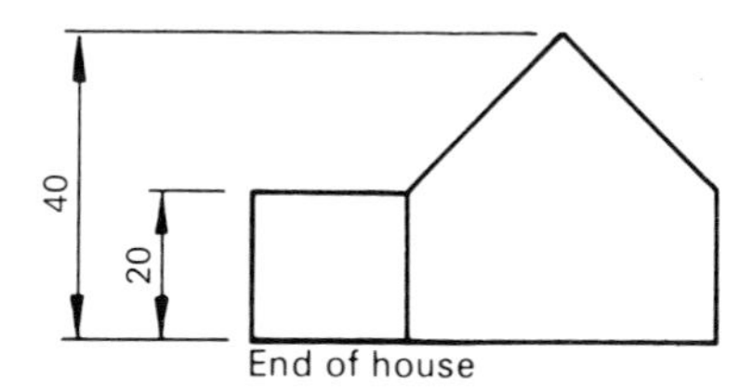

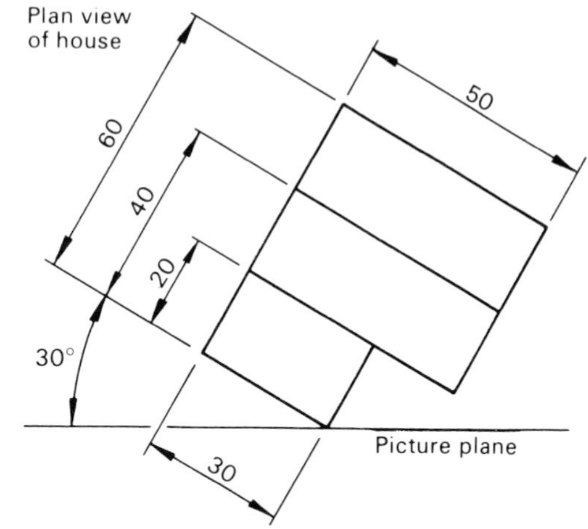

2 The drawings below show views of a train travelling on a concrete monorail. Construct the following perspective views of the train on the rail:

(a) A view from an eye position 45 mm above the top of the train.

(b) A view from an eye position 45 mm below the underside of the train. After completing the usual construction as far as finding the vanishing points, move the horizon to a more convenient position as shown on page 37.

In each case make the station point 175 mm from the picture plane. The distance between the vanishing points will then be 350 mm which will fit on A3 size paper used horizontally.

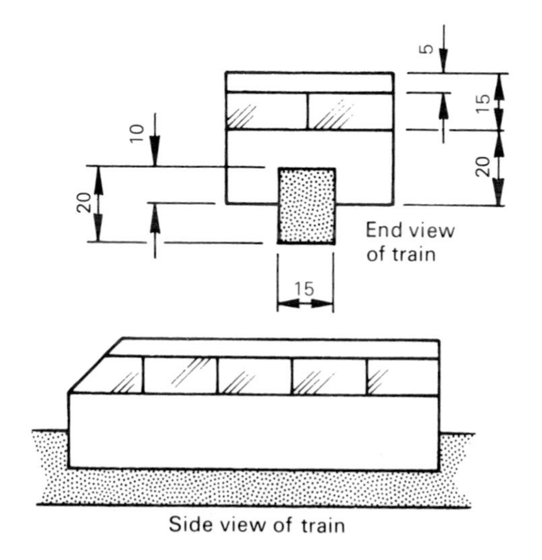

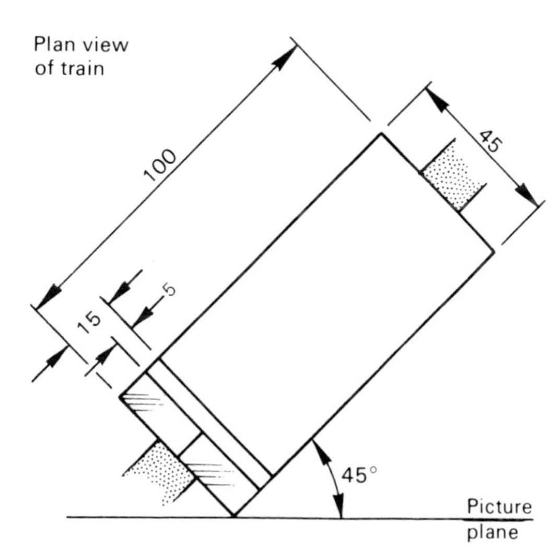

6 Perspective views built up on grids

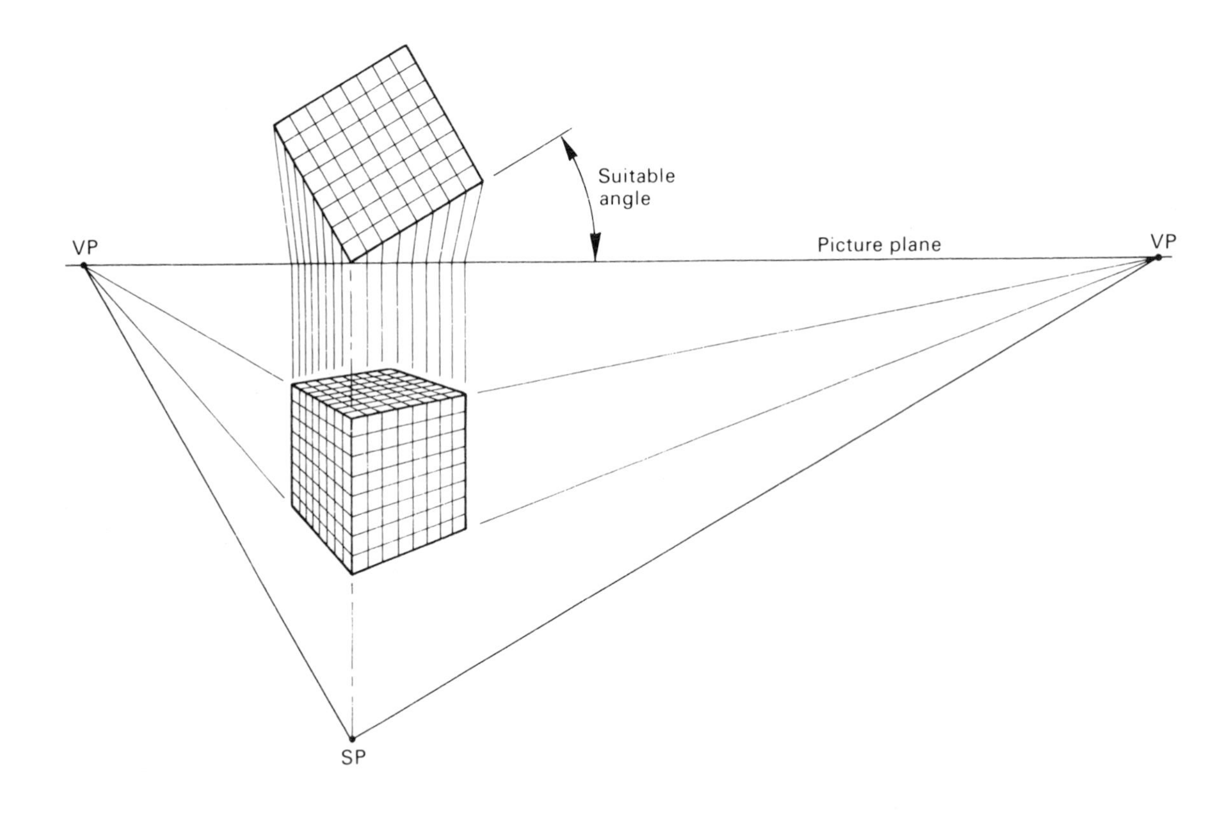

This drawing of a cube divided into a number of smaller cubes has been constructed in the same way as the drawing of the house on page 34. The network of smaller cubes form a grid built up from two vanishing points and provides a guide on which drawings can be made in two-point perspective.
You will remember that when we look down on an object, a third vanishing point is introduced. Although it is possible to construct grids containing three vanishing points, the work in this book will be confined to the more simple two-point grid.
The above grid is too small to work with and must be enlarged to a suitable size as shown on the opposite page.

The enlarged cube

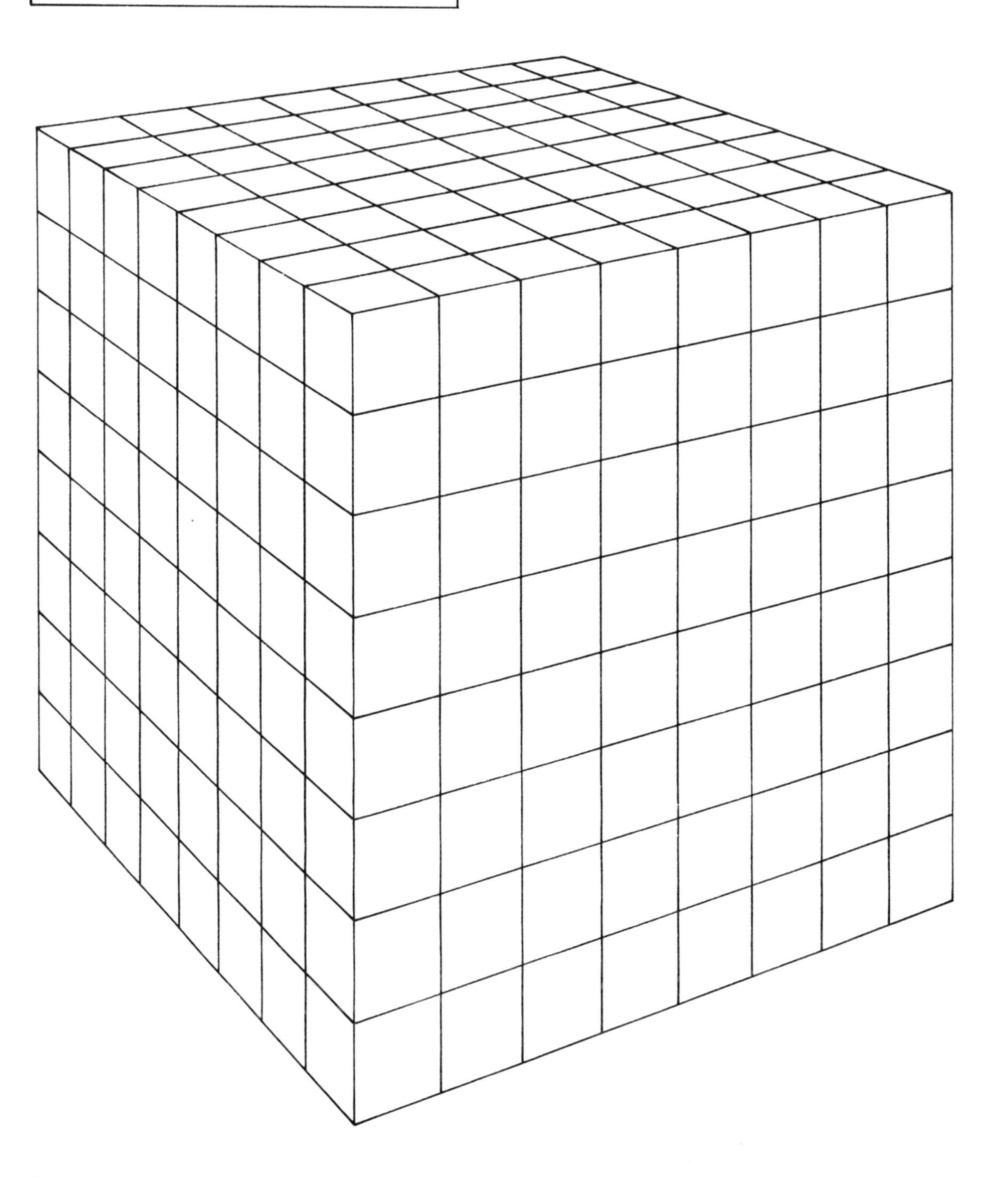

This grid can be traced and then used underneath thin paper to help you produce realistic perspective views.

Sketching using the grid as a guide

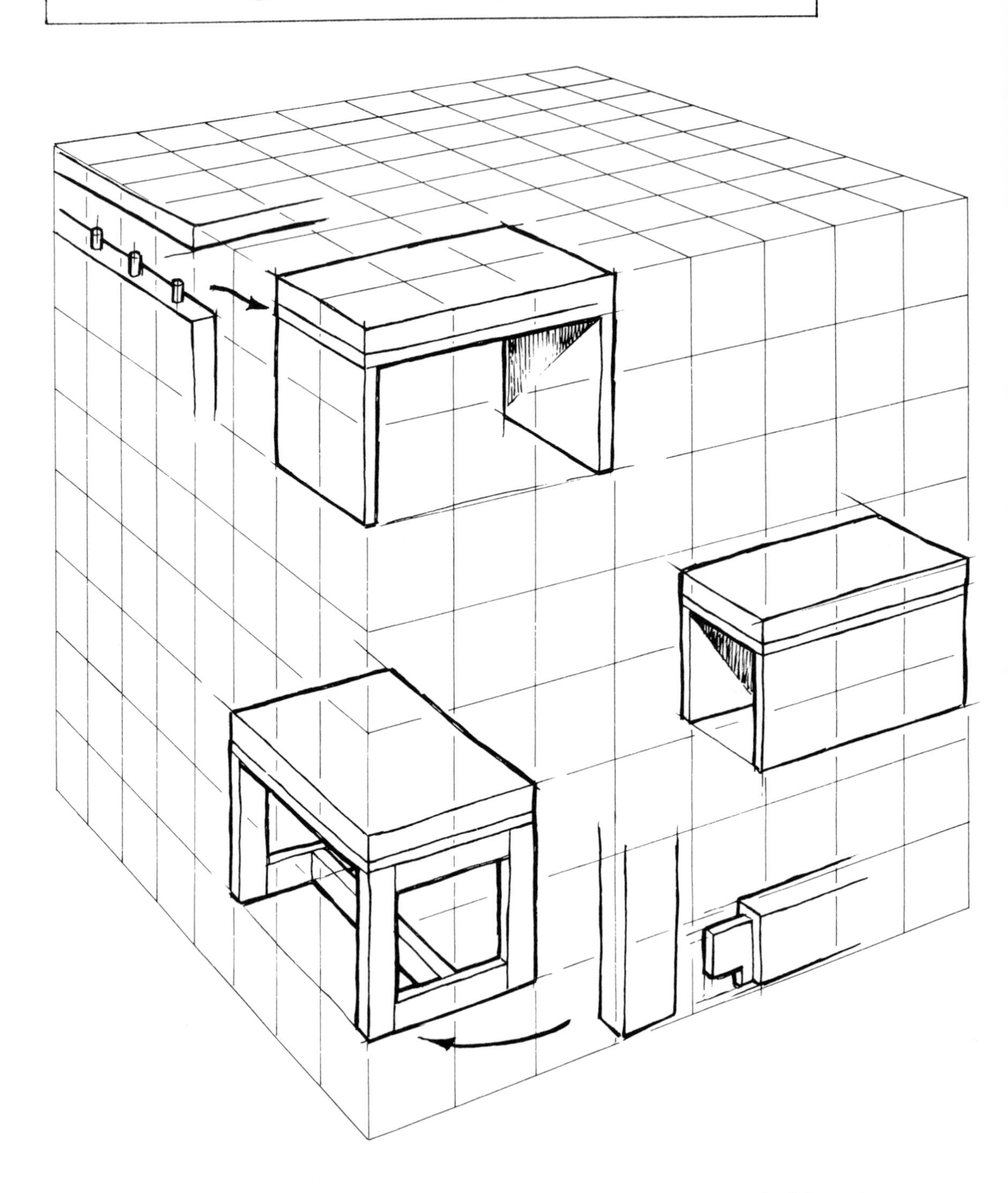

When sketching, it can be helpful to make your drawings over a grid so that, although they are freehand, the perspective is reasonably accurate.

Drawing within the grid

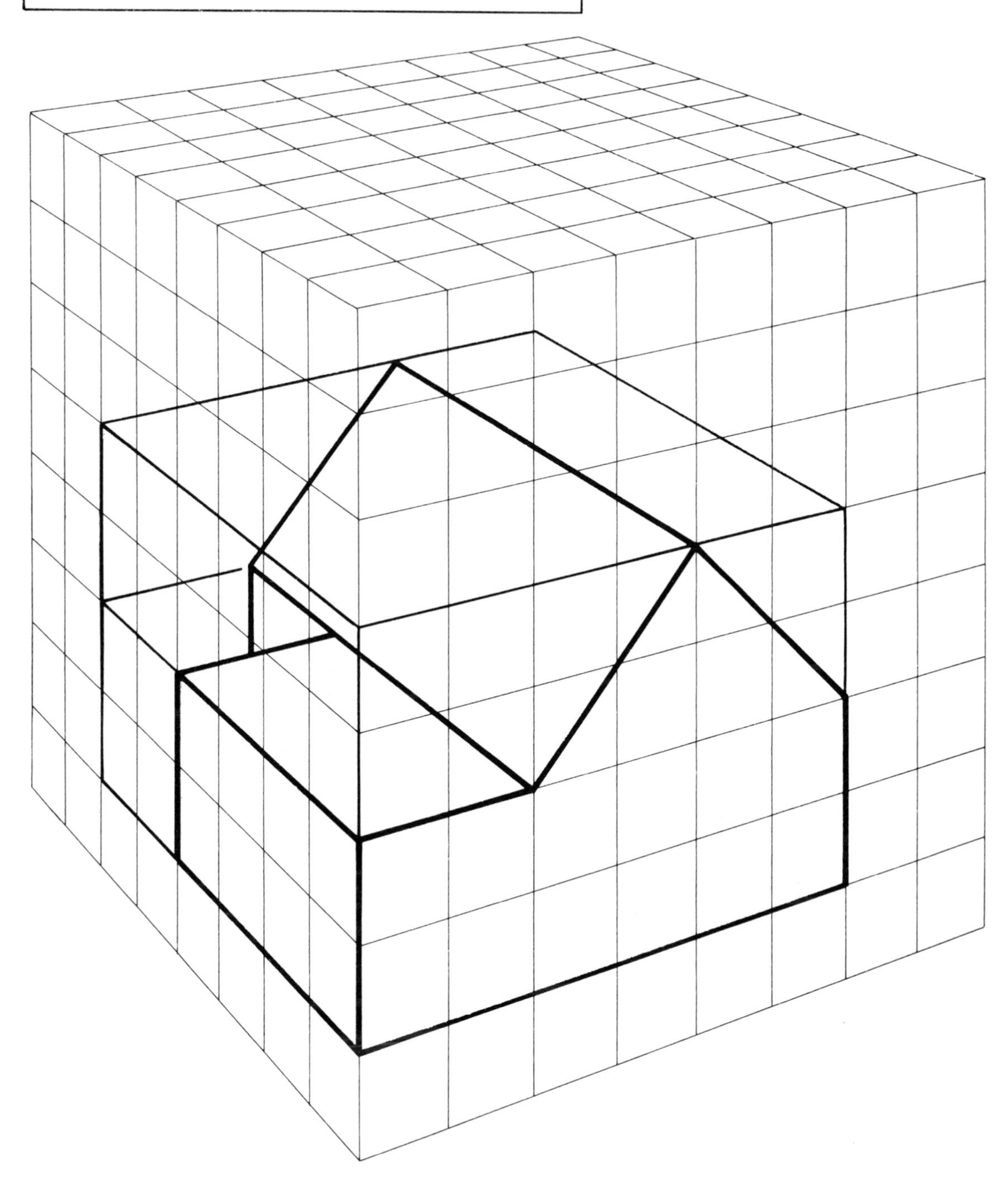

After deciding on a suitable scale, construct a crate in an acceptable position and draw the object within it. Any line of the drawing which fails to coincide with a line of the grid is placed in the direction of the vanishing point using the grid lines for guidance.

Exercise 6a

Trace the perspective grid on page 41 and, with a piece of thin paper over the top of the grid, construct the two drawings shown below. The measurements represent the number of squares that you have to count on the grid.

1 A house

This is the same house as on page 43 but you must construct this particular view.

Construct the view with the top of the crate at the top of the grid and with edge A touching the corner nearest to you.

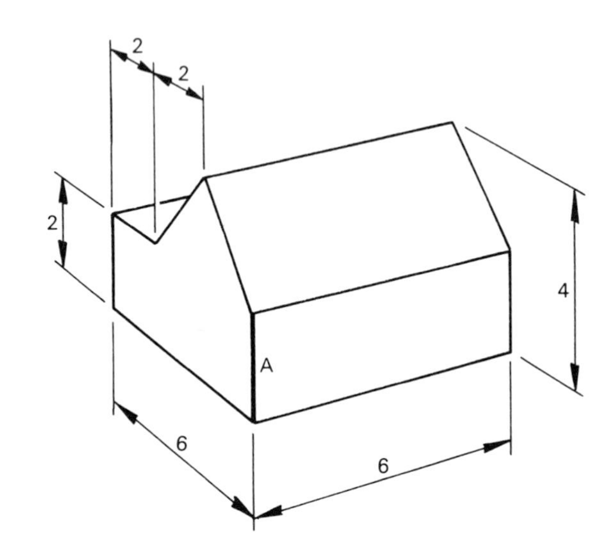

2 Snow cat

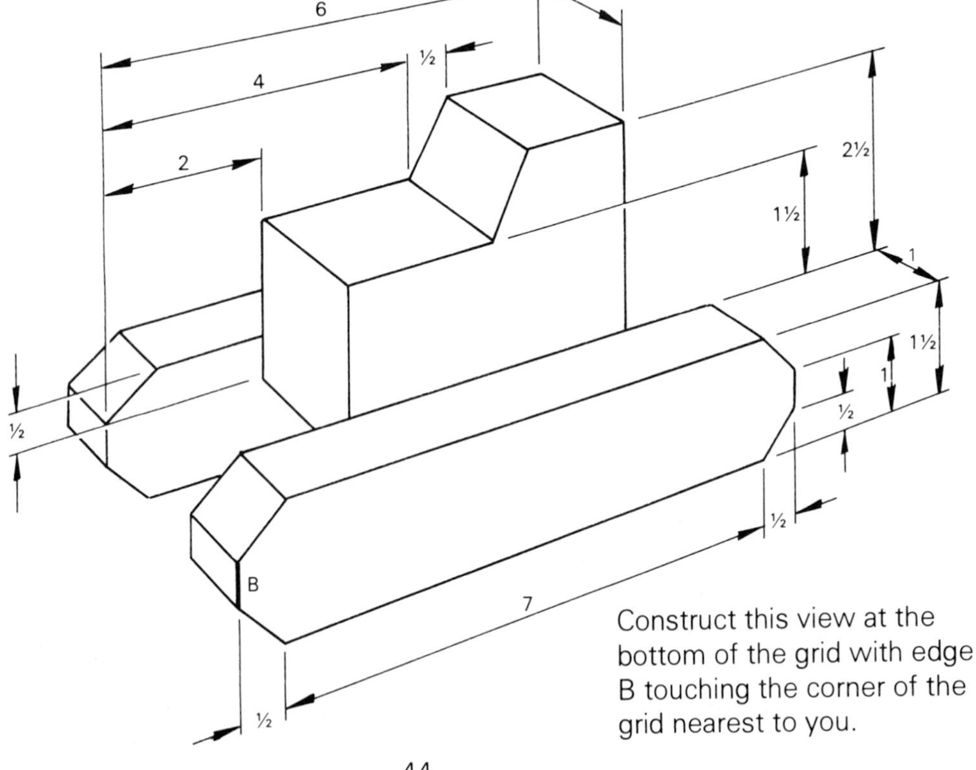

Construct this view at the bottom of the grid with edge B touching the corner of the grid nearest to you.

Different views from one grid

As you can see, your tracing of the grid can be used in four ways to obtain a wide choice of views.

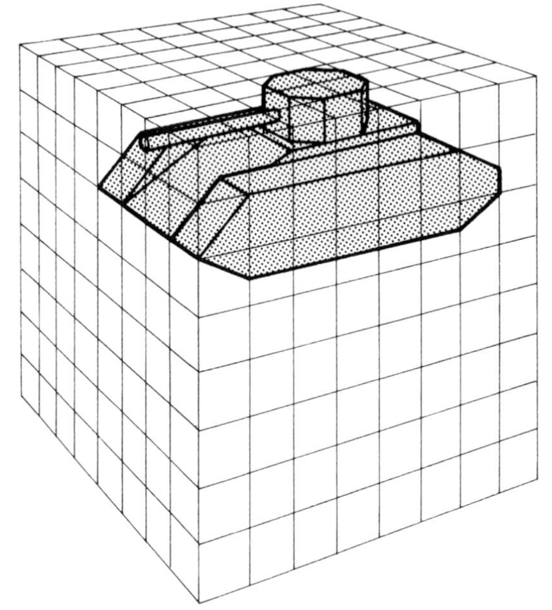

1 As traced.

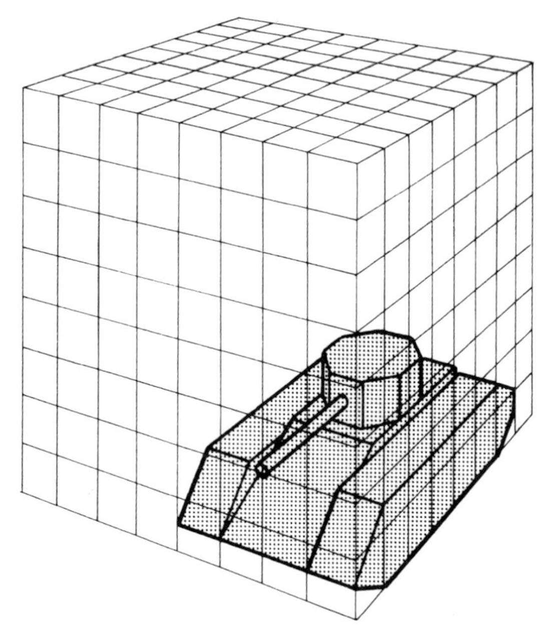

2 With the grid reversed.

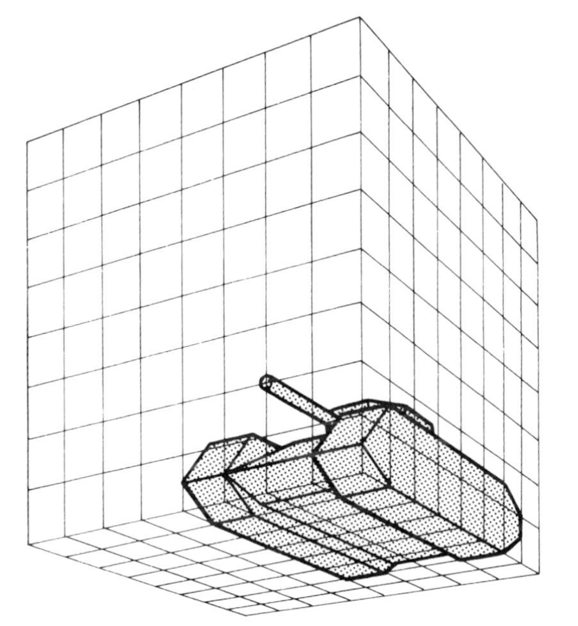

3 Using the grid upside down.

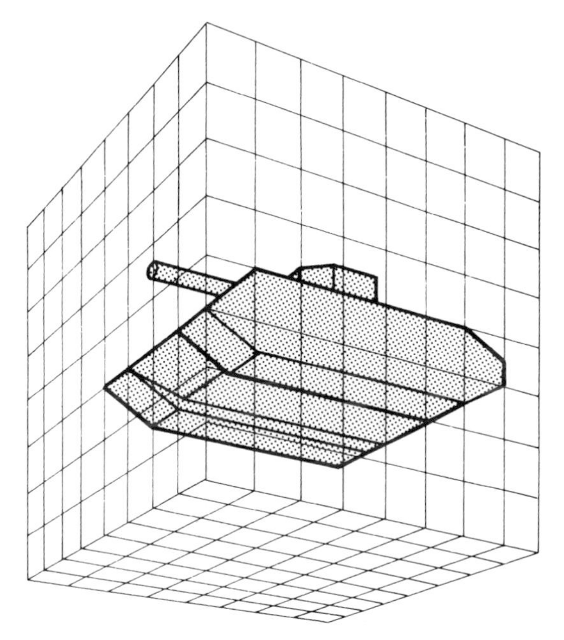

4 With the grid reversed and upside down.

Plotting on a grid from orthographic views

In this example a network of horizontal and vertical lines has been drawn over the views of the jeep. A convenient scale has been chosen so that a square on this grid will correspond to a square of the perspective grid.

The drawing below shows part of a perspective grid on which the crate which is to contain the vehicle has been plotted with some further details added. The edges of the crate have been annotated merely to show the relationship between the views. Note that the ellipses are sketched within squares which have been plotted on the grid.

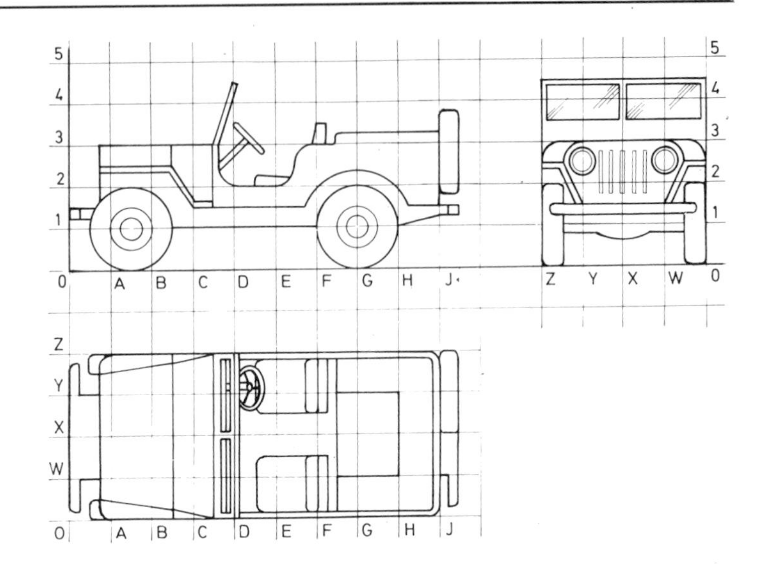

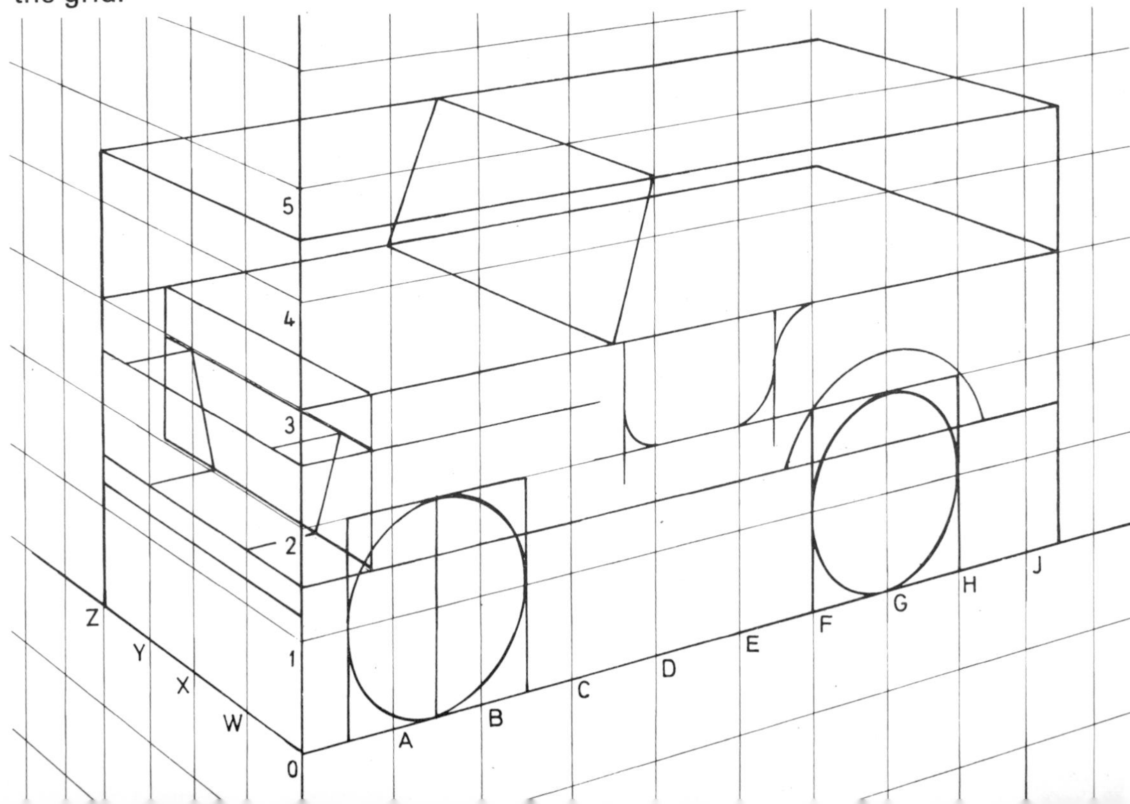

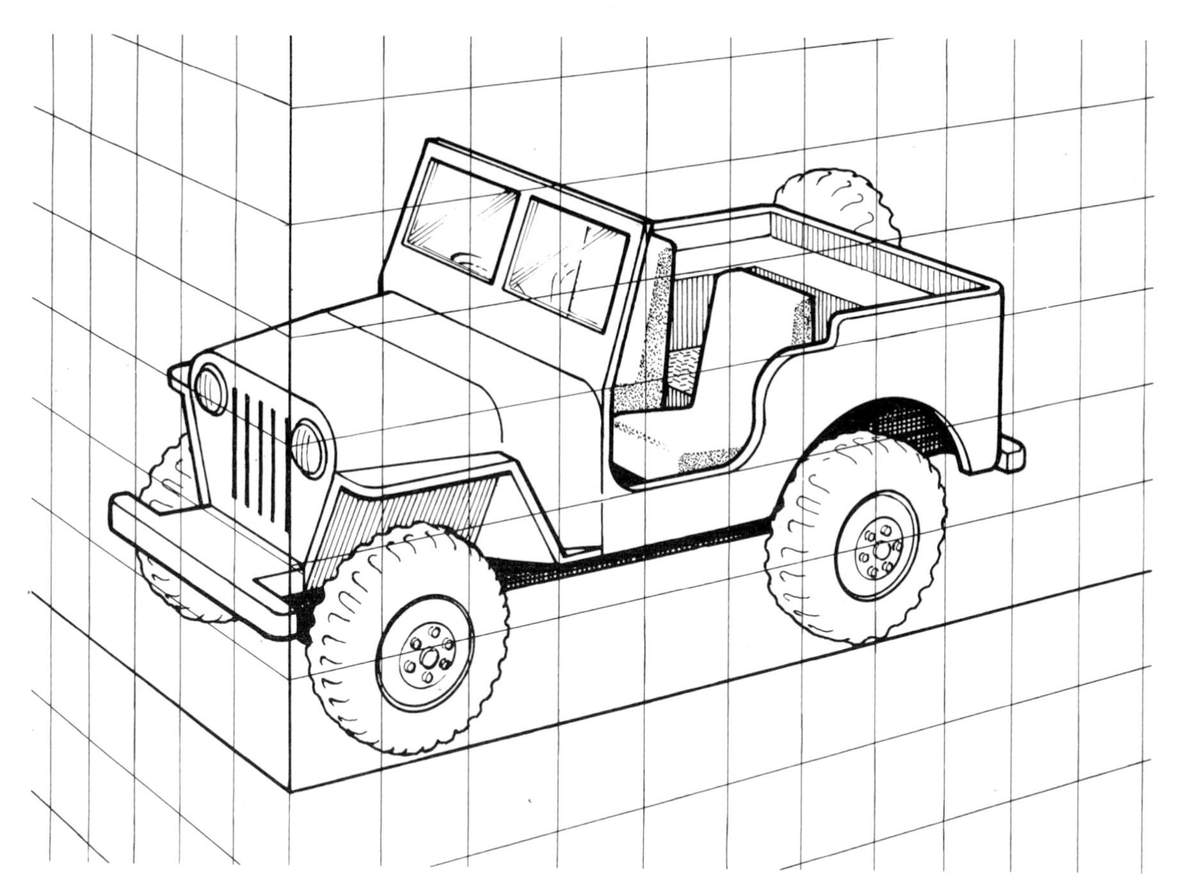

The drawing of the jeep has been completed within the framework shown opposite. Many details of a minor nature can be approximated once the main parts have been completed.

Exercise 6b

Trace the grid on page 48 and construct a view of the ship looking in the direction of arrow A. Make one small square of this grid equal one square of the perspective grid.
Position point X, the lowest corner of the crate which will contain the ship, on point O on the perspective grid.

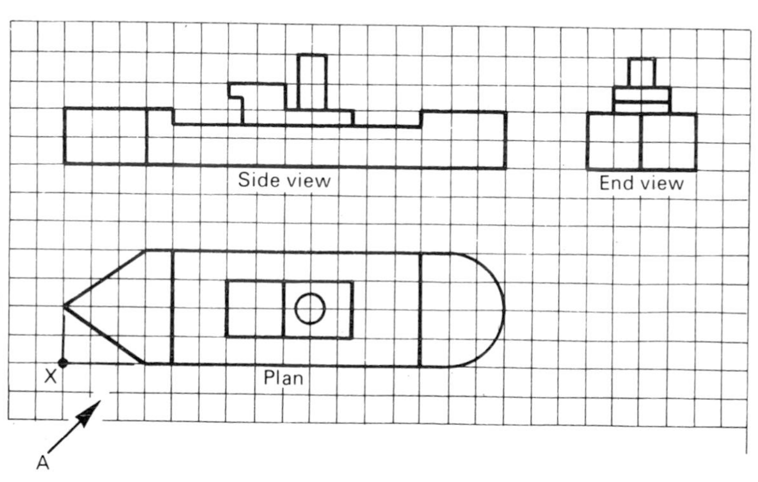

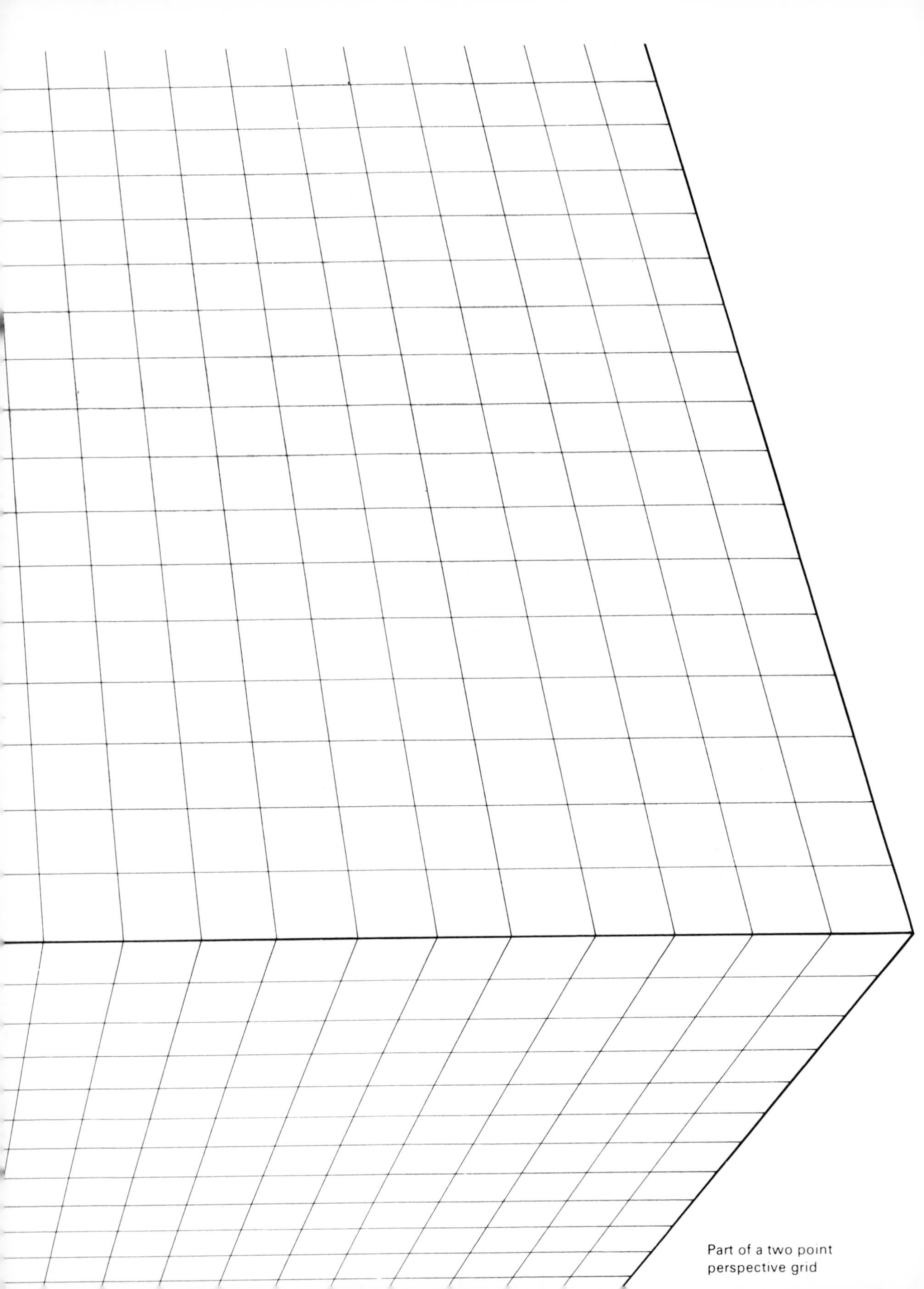

Part of a two point perspective grid

Example drawn on a grid

The camera has been drawn within the grid shown opposite. The body and the other main details were plotted accurately, whereas minor details have been approximated. Ellipses have been sketched within squares which have been constructed on the grid.

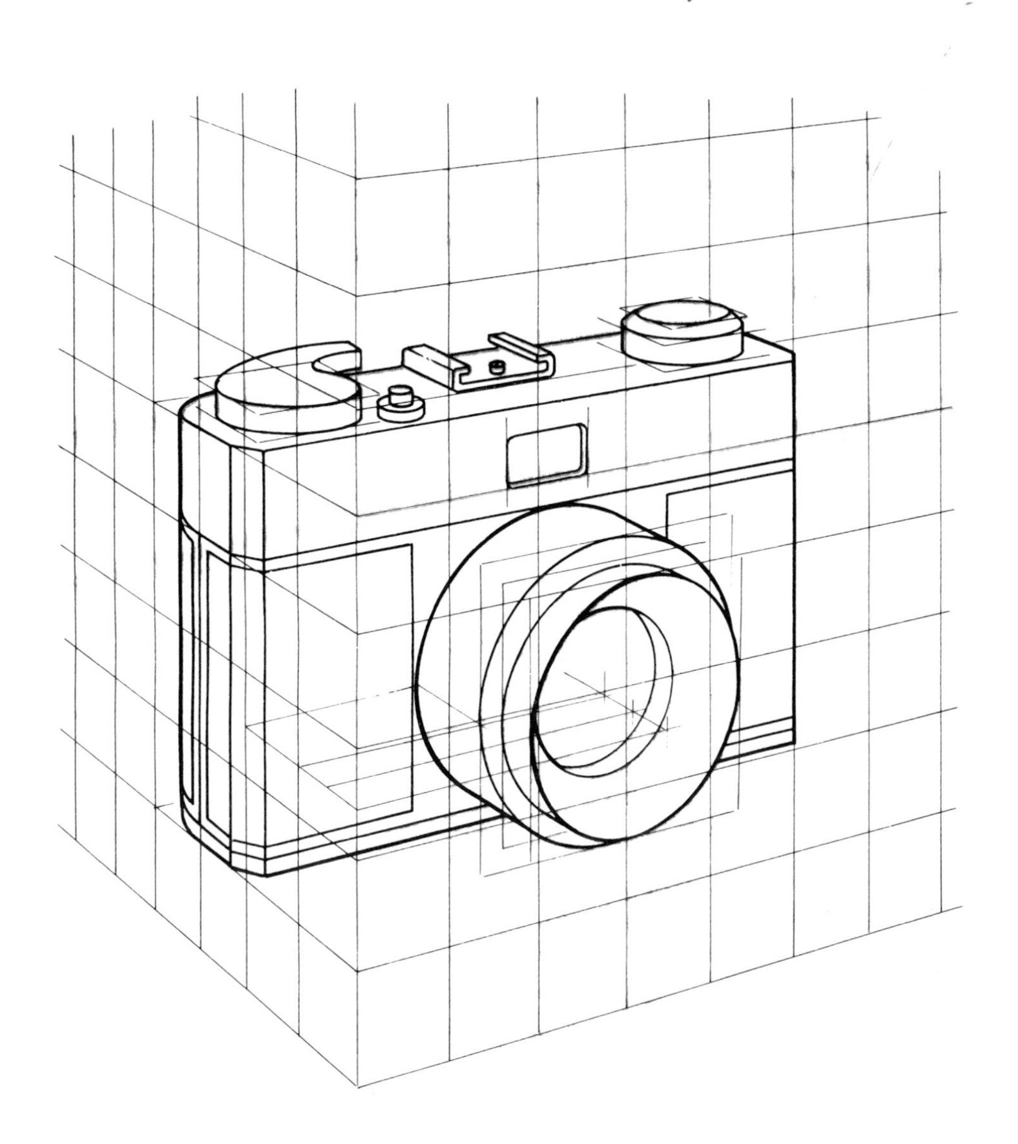

7 Light, shade and form

So far we have only considered line drawing. The use of line is an artificial means whereby we can represent a three-dimensional object on a two-dimensional surface. Lines generally represent edges where two surfaces meet, but when you look at an object you cannot see these lines. In reality we understand the form of an object by the way that light is reflected from its various surfaces and we can see any edges through the change in light reflected by the surfaces. We can make our drawings more realistic by shading or colouring them to take account of the way that light is reflected.

If we wish to make an effective drawing of an object, the factors we have to consider are its form, the position of the source of light, and what happens when light from this source strikes the surfaces of the object.

Most man-made articles can be simplified into standard solid forms. For instance, if we consider this lawnmower, the body consists of a flat T-shaped block on which is placed an irregular four-sided pyramid cut off at the top. The wheels are short cylinders and the handle is also cylindrical.

We then have to decide from which direction the light is coming. It is permissible to imagine the light as coming from any direction which will help in understanding the form of the object, but it is usually placed at one side rather than in a central position. This gives contrast to the edges where surfaces meet and also creates visual interest.

To render a drawing successfully, you must know the standard solid forms and be aware of what happens when light falls on them. The basic forms to be considered in this chapter are the cube, prism, pyramid, cylinder, cone, and sphere.

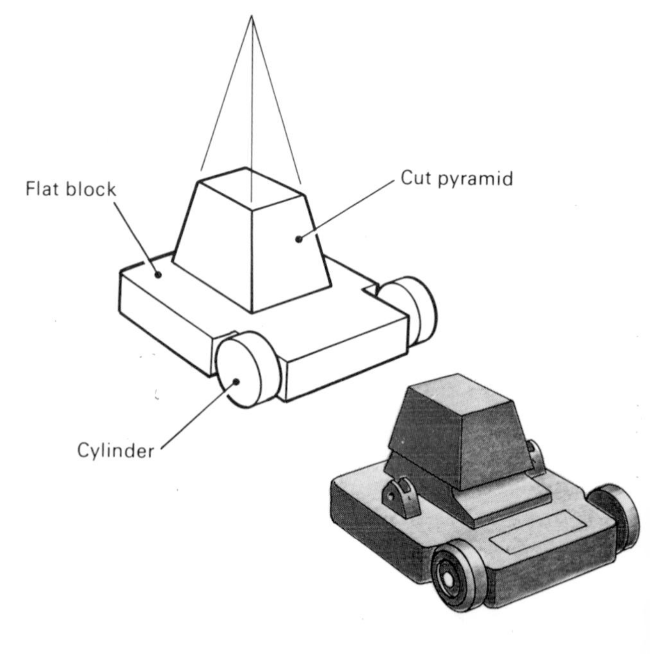

The cube

Here are some cubes in the form of building bricks. You can see that light is reflected from the surfaces in varying amounts; the lighter surfaces are facing towards the light and the darker surfaces are turned away from the light.

This cube has been shaded as if each surface were reflecting the same amount of light. The visual effect is monotonous and uninteresting and, without the lines, the form could be interpreted as a flat hexagonal shape.

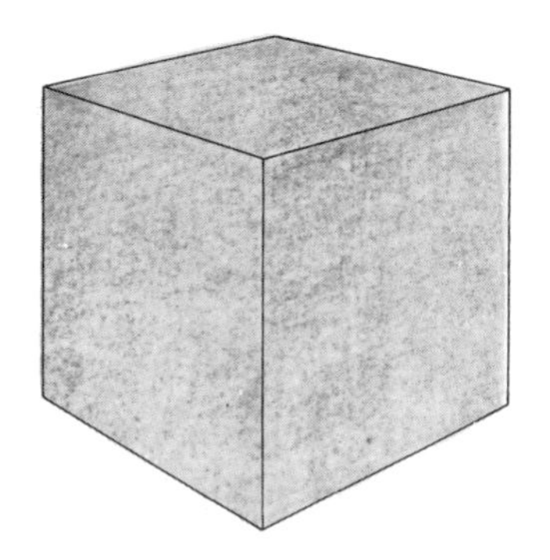

The surfaces of this cube have been shaded as if they were reflecting different amounts of light. This gives a more realistic effect.
Our usual light sources are the sun or artificial illumination, both of which normally spread light from above. Therefore, when shading, we can consider that surfaces facing upwards will reflect most light.
In this example the light source is imagined as being above and to the left of the cube so that the surface on the left appears lighter than the surface on the right. As a general rule, for an object having horizontal and vertical surfaces our shading can fall into three categories, those of light, medium, and dark areas.

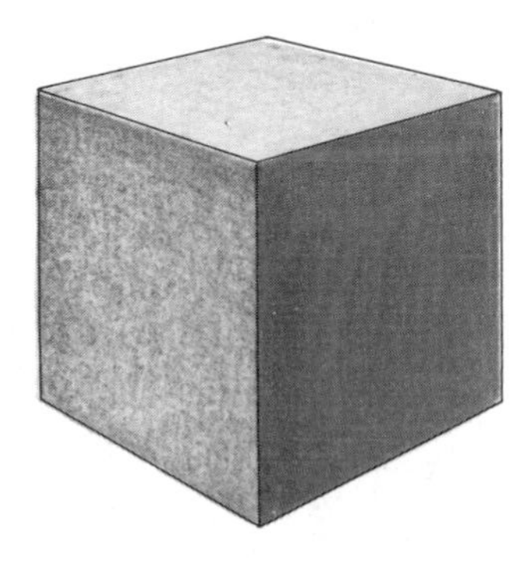

Exercise 7a

This drawing of a simple candle-holder has been shaded as if it was illuminated from high up on the right-hand side. Once again the shading falls roughly into light, medium, and dark areas.
Use your perspective drawing of the decorative wall block made for exercise 1c on page 6 and shade it using a soft pencil. Look at the position in which you have drawn the block and consider the most suitable direction from which light should fall.

The prism

A prism is a solid that has equal shapes at each end and has parallel sides between the ends.
The main body of this children's roundabout is a hexagonal prism having six sides. The surfaces of a prism reflect differing amounts of light. Those nearest the light source reflect most light and less light is reflected as the surfaces turn away from the light.

Here are some examples of regular prisms with varying numbers of sides. The light falls from the top left and in front of each prism.

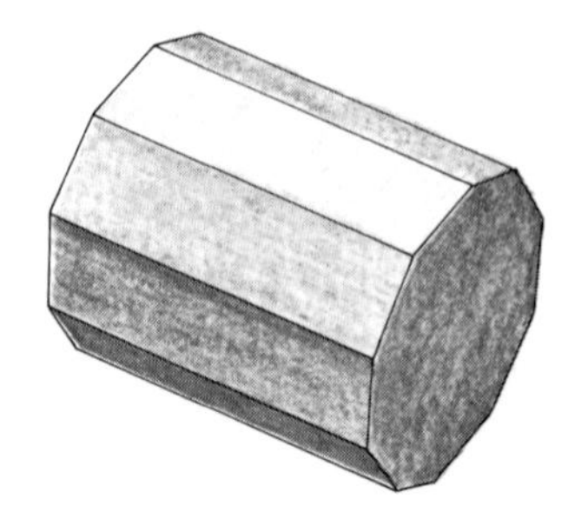

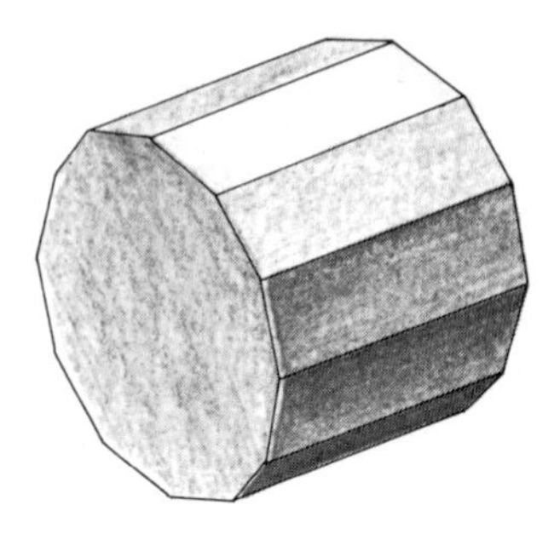

Exercise 7b

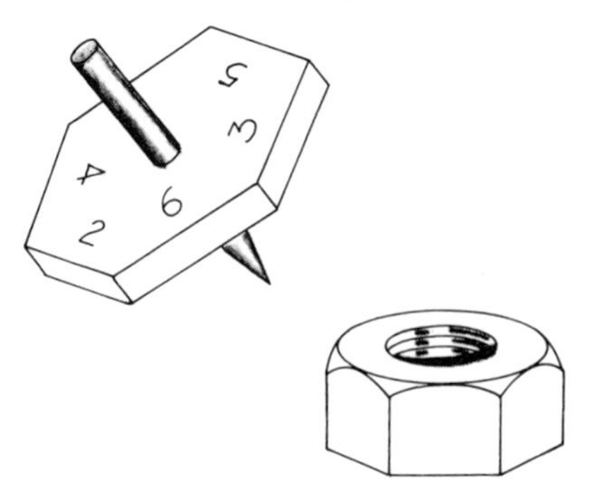

Each of these objects is based on the hexagonal prism. Draw them about twice this size and shade them assuming that the light falls from a high point on the right-hand side.
Use a coloured pencil if you wish, varying the pressure to provide the contrast between the surfaces.

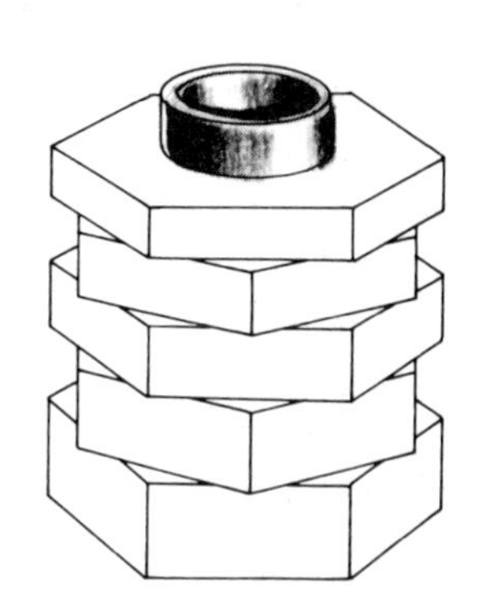

The pyramid

The pyramid differs from the prism in that the sides taper to a point which is called the apex. The surfaces reflect less light as they turn away from the light source. A pyramid pointing upwards will reflect more light than one pointing downwards.

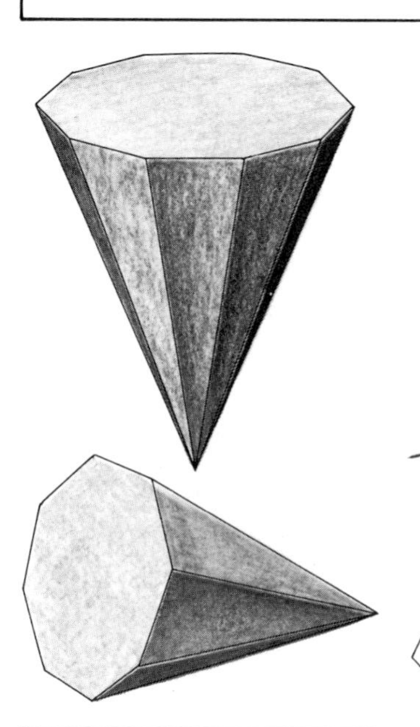

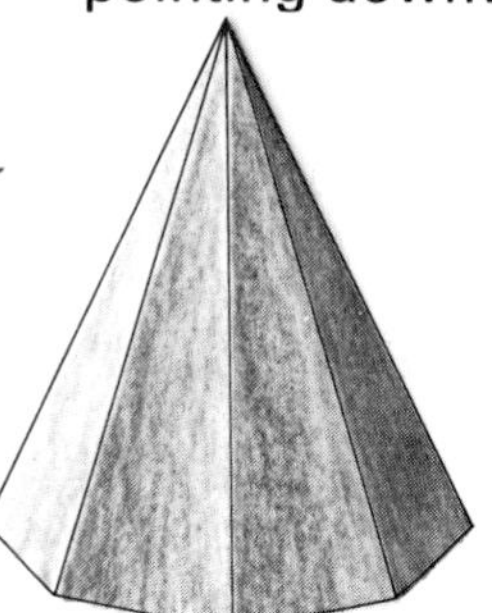

Exercise 7c

Copy the drawing of the pepper pot, about half as big again as it is printed here, and shade it as if the light were coming from high up on the left-hand side.
Sketch the axes and ellipses to help you build up your drawing.

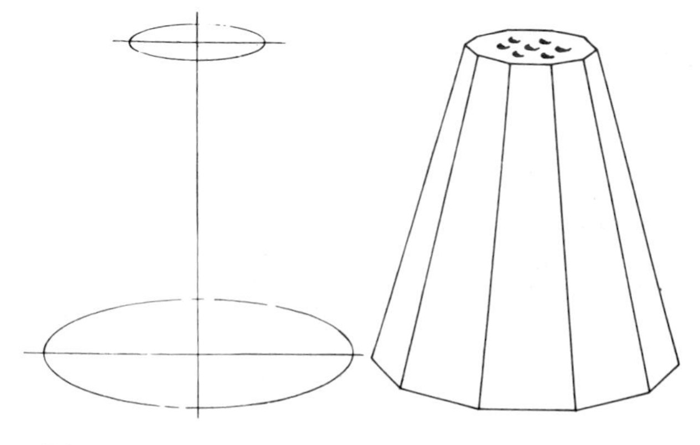

The cylinder

A cylinder has equal parallel circular ends joined by a body with parallel edges.
The body of the letter box is an example of a cylinder. Since the surface of a cylinder is curved and continuous, the amount of light that is reflected gradually gets less as the surface turns away from the light.
When shading a curved surface, try to avoid placing the lightest area at the centre of the object. If this lightest area is positioned off-centre, as in the example below, more visual interest is created because the shading varies in each half of the drawing.

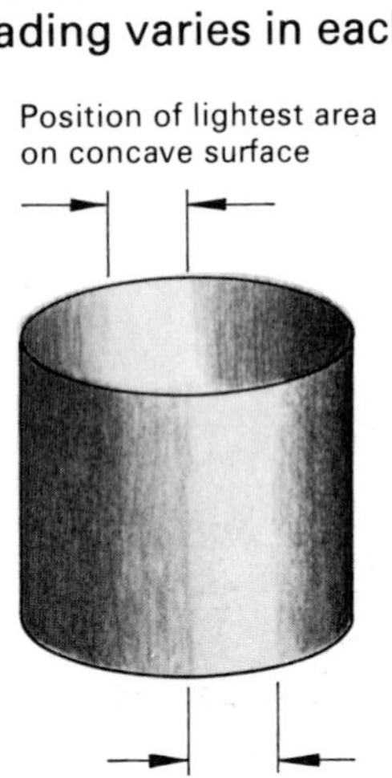

This drawing shows an open cylinder. When light falls on the inside, or concave, surface, the main areas of highlight and shadow are opposite to those on the outside, or convex, surface.

Exercise 7d

The forms of these objects are based on cylinders. Copy the drawings about twice this size and shade them imagining light falls on them from a suitable source.

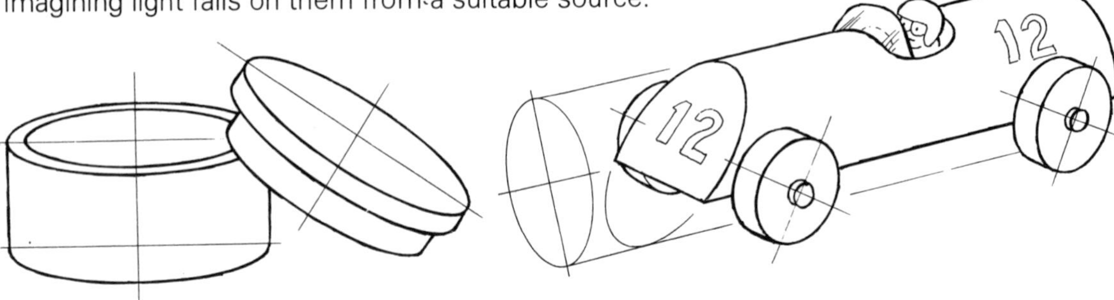

The cone

A cone has a circular base with sides which taper towards the apex. These hazard cones are basically conical forms.
The effect of light on a cone follows the same principle as for a cylinder except for the obvious tapering to the pointed end.
Cones are also similar to pyramids in that upward pointing cones reflect more light than downward pointing cones.

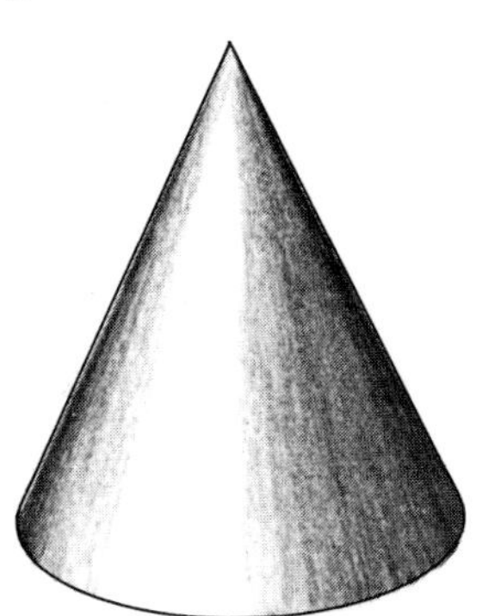

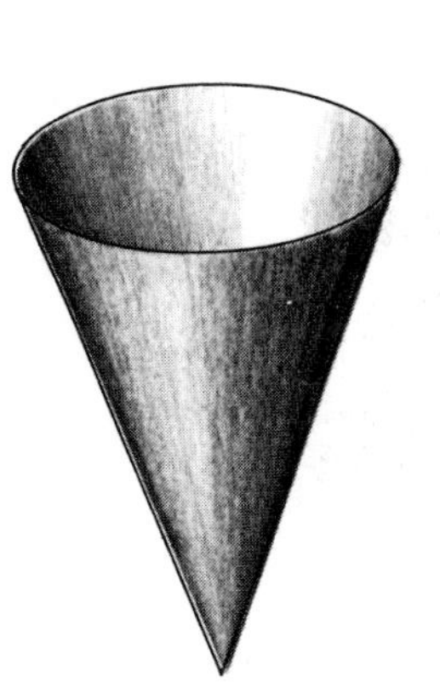

Exercise 7e

Trace this drawing and shade it assuming that light falls from a point high up on the left-hand side.

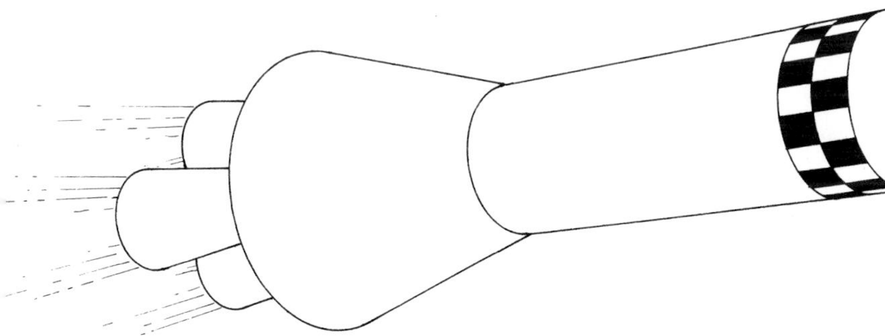

The sphere

A sphere is a round solid body. These balls from various games are all spherical.
The part of a sphere nearest to the light source will reflect most light and less light is reflected as the surface curves away from the light.

Exercise 7f

Sketch this ornament about twice this size and shade it with coloured pencils according to how light is reflected from a suitable light source.
A suggested colour scheme is blue for the head, body, and tail, yellow beak and legs, with a green base.

Shaded examples taking into account the effect of light

In these examples the light falls on the articles from the right-hand side. There would also be some shadows as a result of the effect of the light, but these have been neglected because they will be dealt with fully in the next chapter.

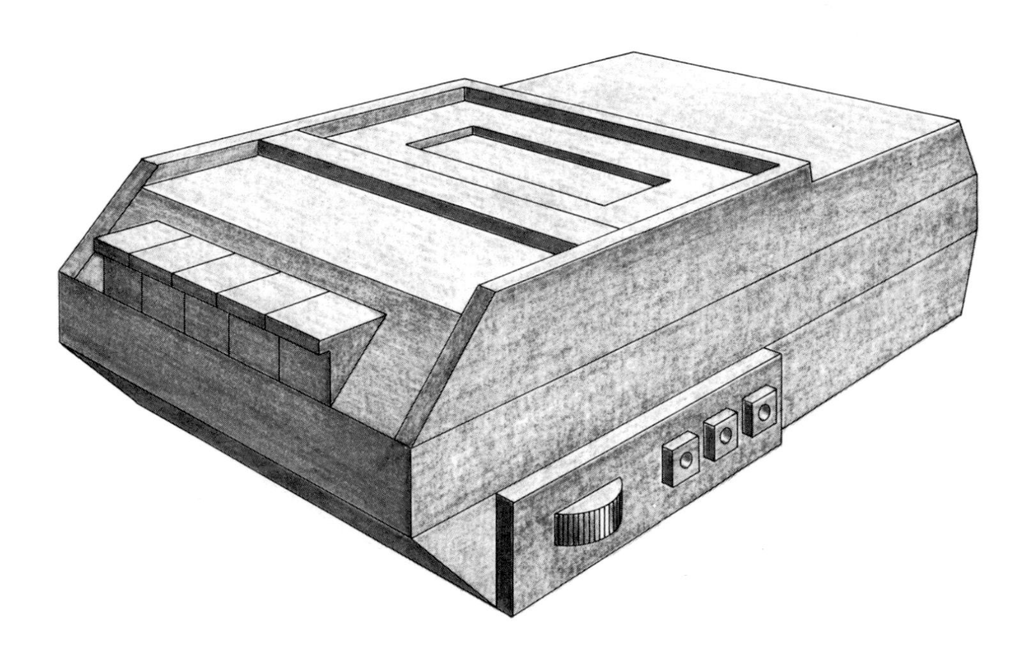

Exercise 7g

This drawing of a microscope has been simplified, as far as possible, into the basic geometric solids.
Trace the illustration and, after first deciding on the position of a suitably placed light source, use a soft pencil to shade the various forms of the object.

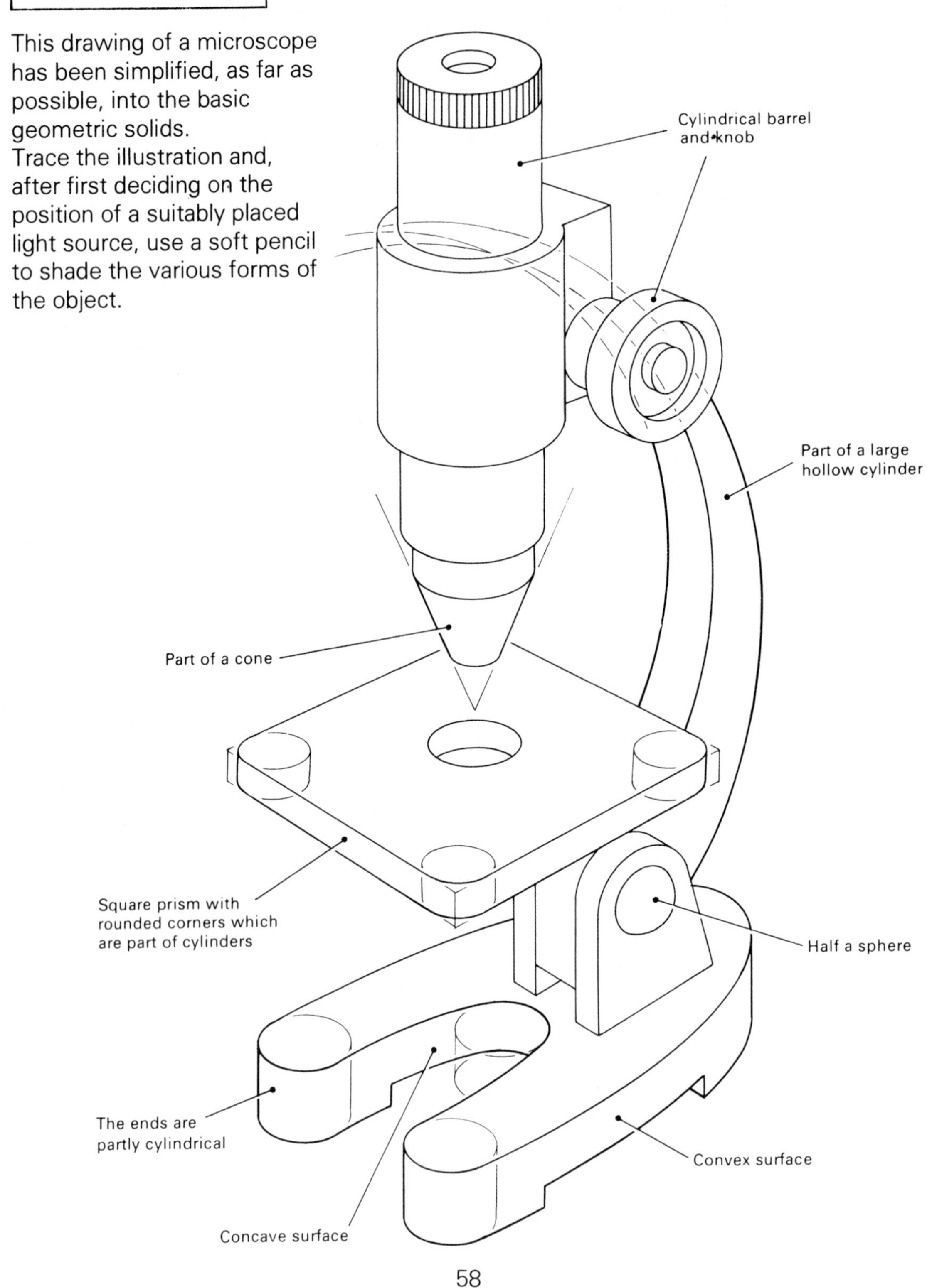

8 Shadows and reflections

As we have seen in Chapter 7, we recognize form by the way that light is reflected from the various surfaces of an object. Direct light, such as light from an electric light bulb or bright sunlight falling on an object, will produce shadows cast on other surfaces.

The pictures below show ways in which shadows are helpful to us in everyday life. We can use these visual clues in our drawings to make them more realistic.

Shadows help to show the change in the direction of surfaces.

Shadows indicate depth in holes and recesses.

A shadow provides stability and a setting for an object.

Shadows give clues to help identify form.

Shadows can indicate protrusions and provide visual interest by contrasting areas of light and shade.

Factors that affect a cast shadow

There are three main factors that determine the shape and position of a cast shadow.

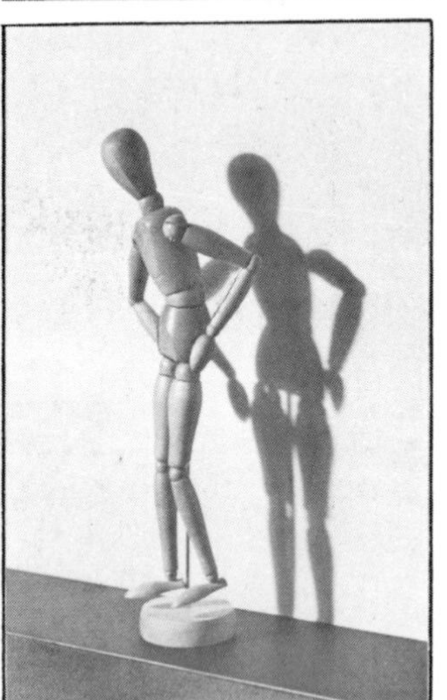

1 The position of the light source in relation to the object.
  The position of the light source that illuminates the figure in the right-hand picture is much lower than that for the one on the left. As a result the shadows differ. The shadow in the picture on the right seems unnatural and menacing probably because, as we have seen, our normal source of light is from above and not below. This type of lighting is used in the theatre and on films for special effects.
2 The shape of the shadow follows the shape of the object.
  In this pair of pictures, the figure has the same light source but is posed in different positions.
3 The shadow follows the form of the surface on which it falls.
  In these examples, the positions of the light source and the figure do not change. The surface on which the shadow falls does vary, however. A box-shaped piece of card is positioned at different heights to show the change in the shape of the shadow.

Exercise 8a

Describe, in words, what is causing the shadow of each person to assume its particular shape. Your answers should define either the form of the surface or an object that would cause this effect.

Constructing cast shadows

Through practice, cast shadows can be sketched and appear realistic. It is possible, however, to construct shadows accurately if the relative positions of the object and the light source are known.
There are two types of shadows that can be constructed:

1 Shadows produced by a light source which is near to the object.
(This covers artificial light sources such as candles, torches, car headlights and electric lights from which the rays of light spread.)
2 Shadows produced by a distant light source.
(Sunlight is the main concern here since the rays of light that strike the object are considered to be parallel.)

Shadows constructed using a 'near' light source

The rectangular shape is illuminated from the light source L. To find the resulting shadow, first mark point P on the surface on which the shape is standing and in a position vertically below the light source.
From the light source draw lines through the corners A and B that will cast shadows. From P draw lines through points A_1 and B_1 (these lie on the ground vertically below A and B). The corners of the shadow are where the pairs of lines intersect, at X and Y. The shadow can now be completed.

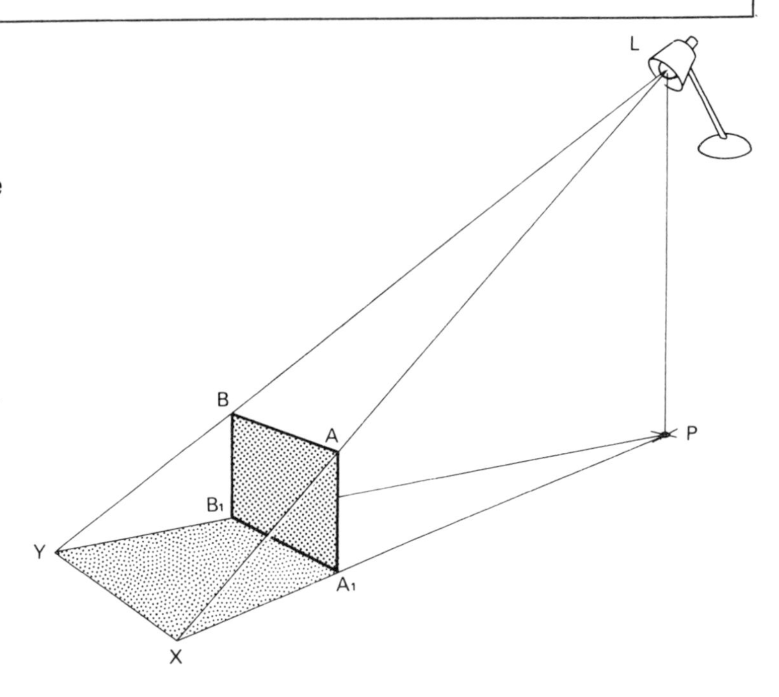

The rectangular shape above has been incorporated into the solid block in this example. Only three corners will cast shadows, A and B as we have seen, and C. D is the nearest corner to the light source and will not cast a shadow.
Point C_1 on the ground below corner C is hidden by the block. It can be found by drawing the dashed lines to complete the hidden detail of the block. Point Z, the shadow of corner C, must be plotted so that the shadow of the block can be completed.

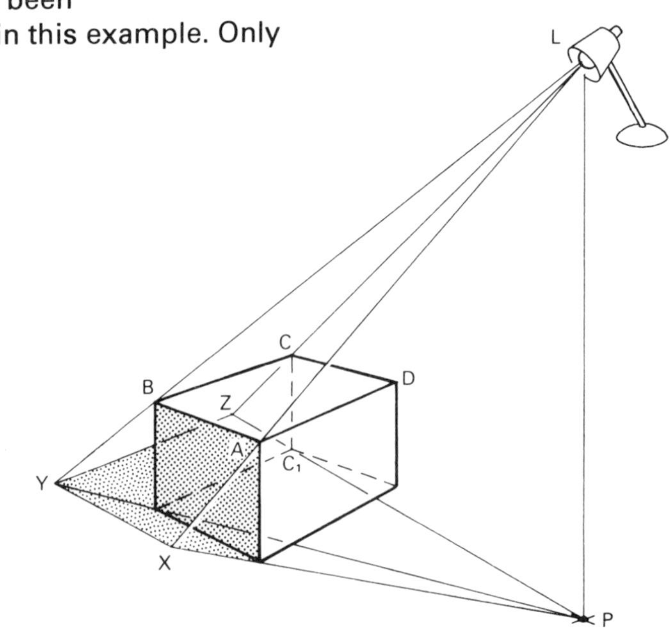

Here is another example of a cast shadow produced by light from a single-point light source. Note that the lines shown dotted are necessary to complete the construction accurately.

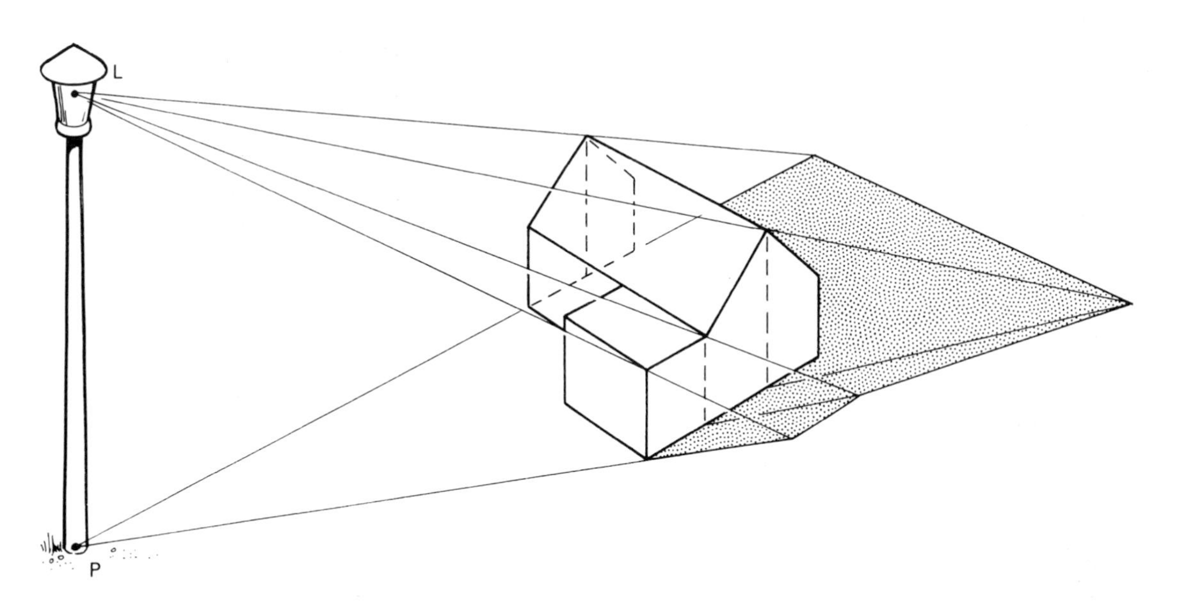

Exercise 8b

Trace this drawing and find the shadow of the books cast by the light from the candle. Allow 60 millimetres to the right of the books for the shadow.

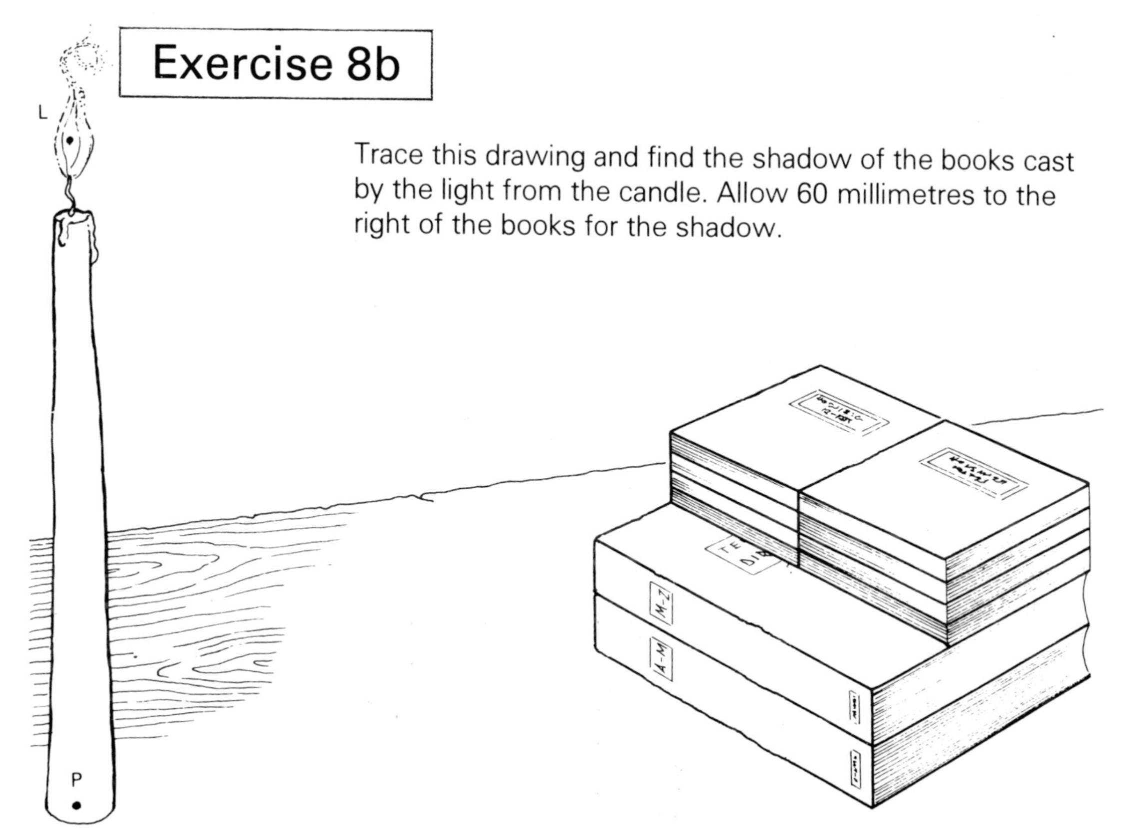

Shadows of curved surfaces

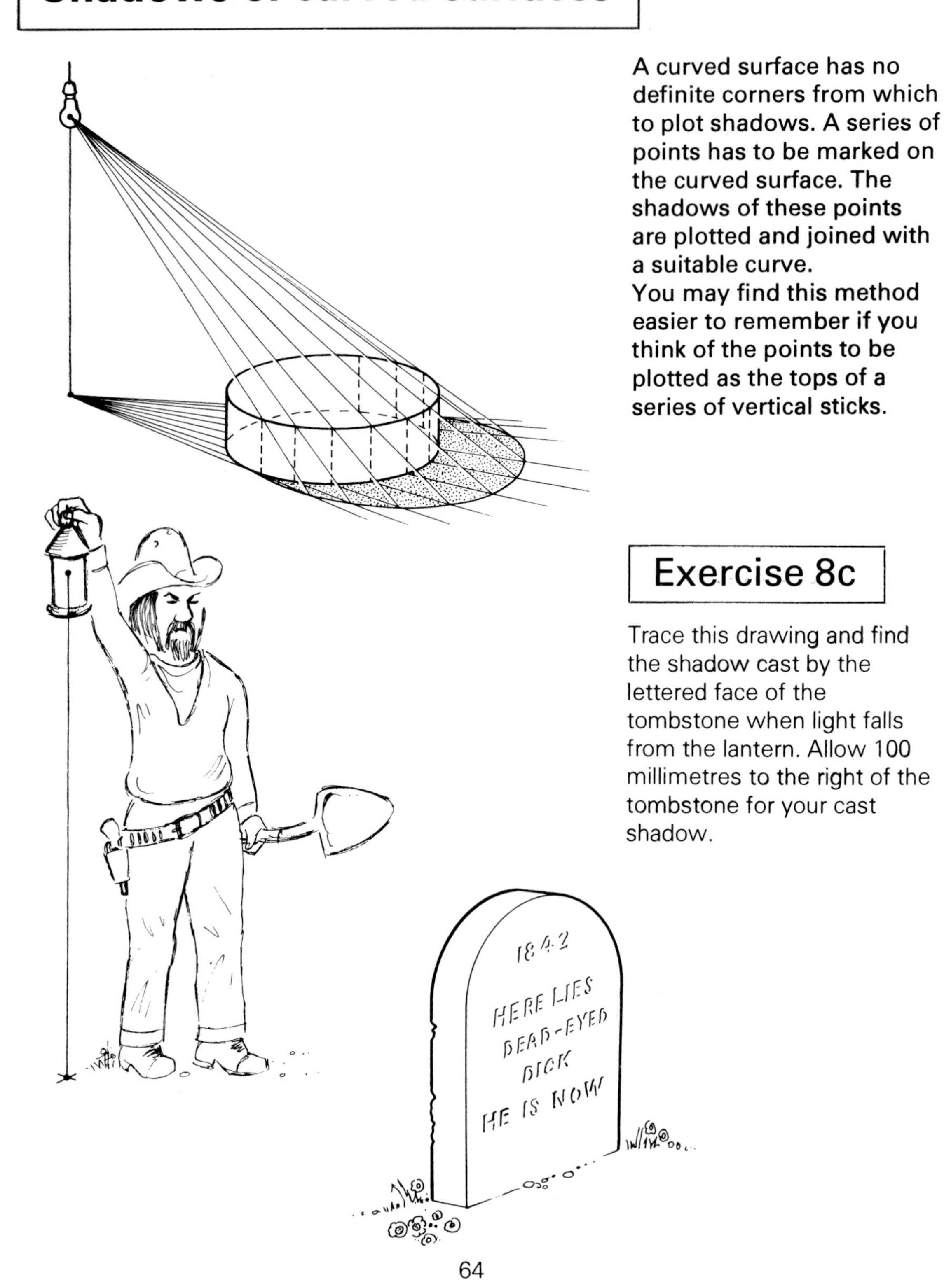

A curved surface has no definite corners from which to plot shadows. A series of points has to be marked on the curved surface. The shadows of these points are plotted and joined with a suitable curve.
You may find this method easier to remember if you think of the points to be plotted as the tops of a series of vertical sticks.

Exercise 8c

Trace this drawing and find the shadow cast by the lettered face of the tombstone when light falls from the lantern. Allow 100 millimetres to the right of the tombstone for your cast shadow.

Finding the shadow in a recess

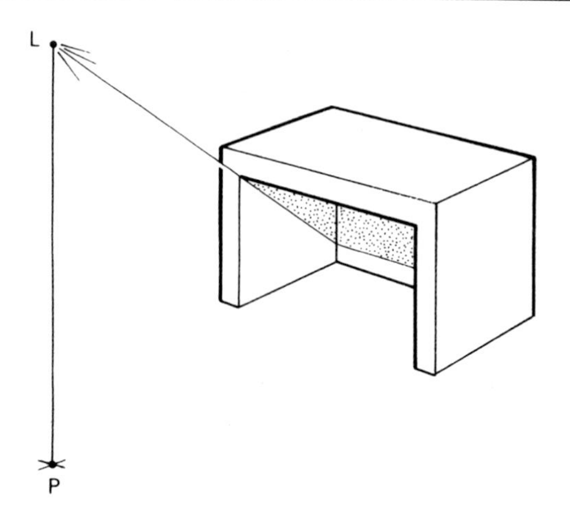

We have seen how shadows in holes and recesses help to indicate depth. These drawings show how to find the shape of a shadow falling inside a box from a single-point light source.

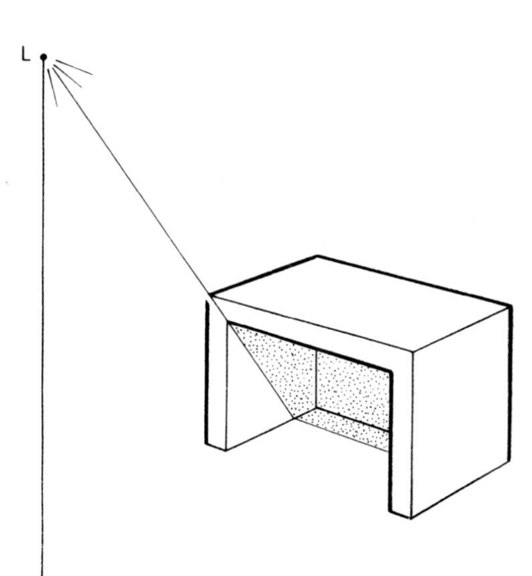

In this case, first join P to the point where the dashed line meets the bottom of the box. The line that passes through the lower inside corner and meets line LP at P_1 should go to the same vanishing point as the line from P. Then follow the construction shown above.

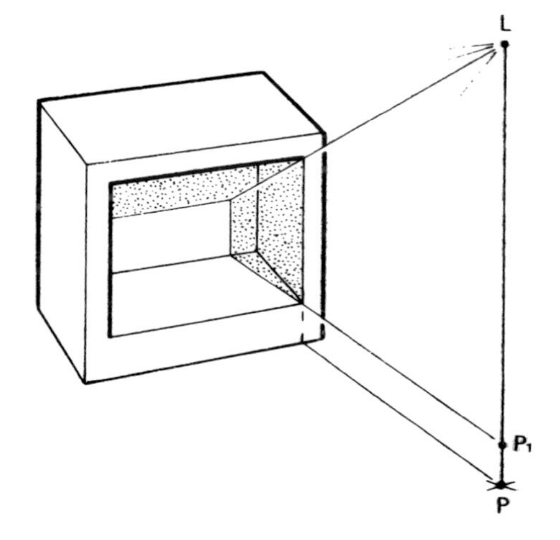

Exercise 8d

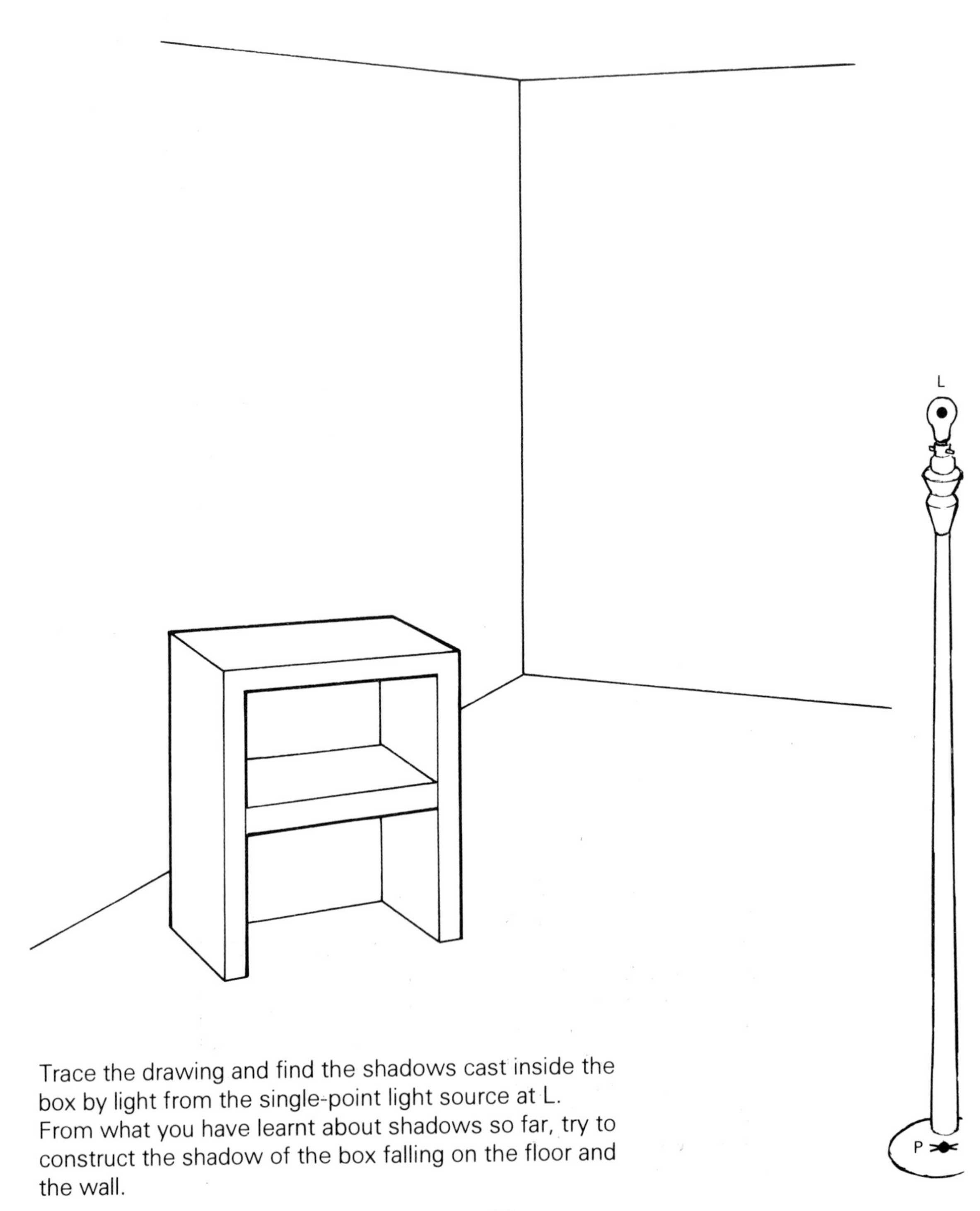

Trace the drawing and find the shadows cast inside the box by light from the single-point light source at L. From what you have learnt about shadows so far, try to construct the shadow of the box falling on the floor and the wall.

Shadows produced by a distant light source

When we consider the cast shadow produced when an object is lit by a distant light source, the exact source of light has to be approximated.
The construction is similar to that used for the single-point light source except that the rays of light and the plan views of the rays on the ground are sets of parallel lines. As before, the pairs of lines intersect to form the corners of the cast shadow. Finding the cast shadow with a distant light source for a curved surface or a shadow in a recess follows the same method as for a single-point light source except that, as above, the rays of light are represented by parallel lines.

Exercise 8e

Find the cast shadow of the jail when sunlight falls on it from the direction shown. Trace the drawing leaving 50 millimetres to the right of the jail for the shadow.

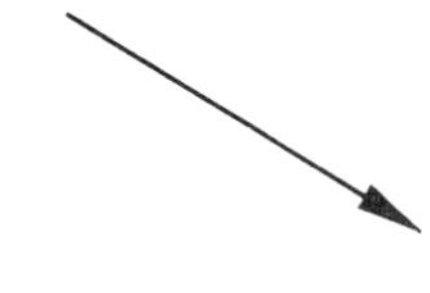

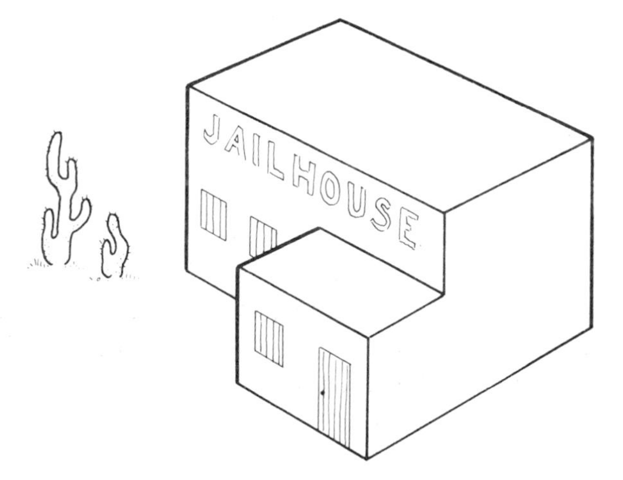

Reflections

A reflection is seen in a smooth surface and is produced by forms outside that surface.
This picture, from an advertisement, is an excellent example of the use of a reflection. It indicates that the car is standing on a surface without distracting one's eye.
In fact, the reflection merely returns one's gaze to the vehicle while at the same time reinforcing its clean lines and perfect finish.
We too can use reflections in our drawings to indicate smooth surfaces and to provide a surface for an object to stand on. These can be very simple with no real indication of shape.

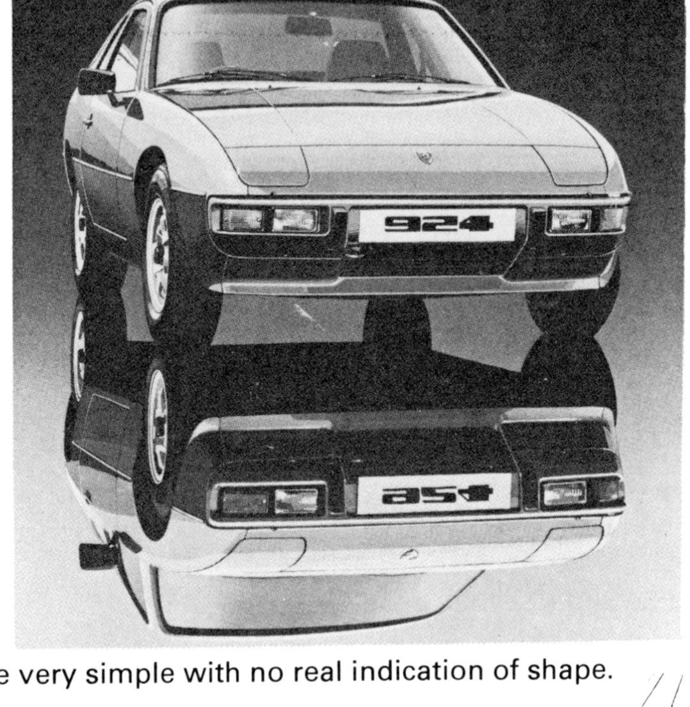

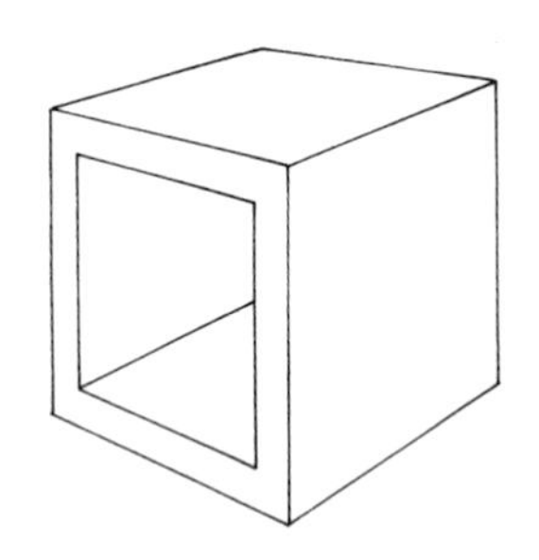

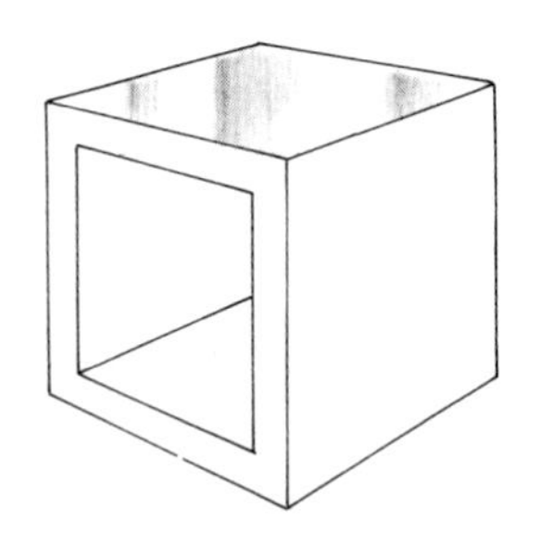

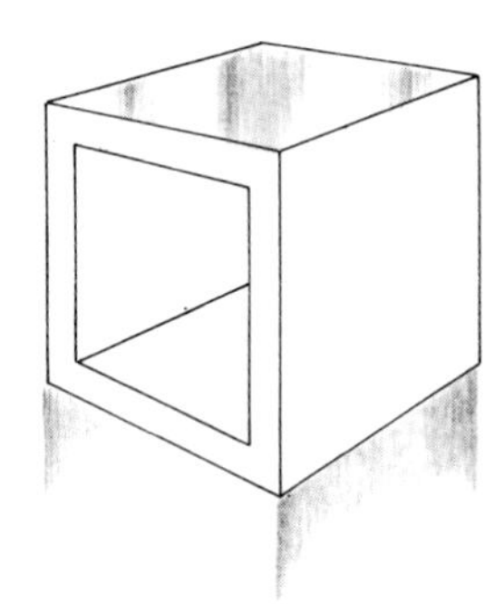

You will have noticed that a reflection is a mirrored image of the item in view and, since most objects in our environment stand vertically, it is best to show vertical reflections as in the drawings above rather than reflections set at an angle or horizontally. Sometimes, however, angled reflections are useful. For instance, the vertical reflections on the top of this solid cylinder give the false impression that it is hollow.

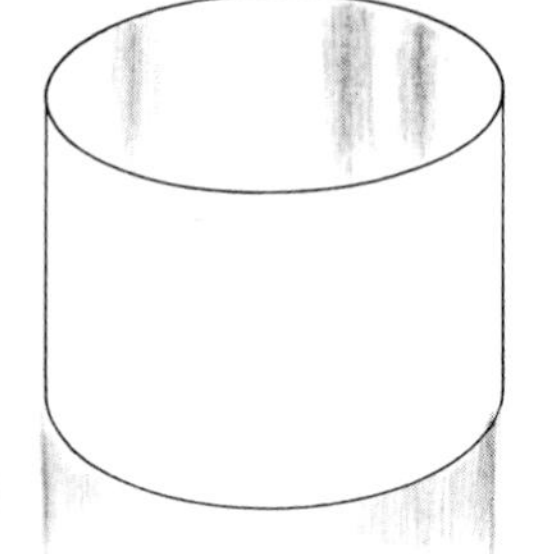

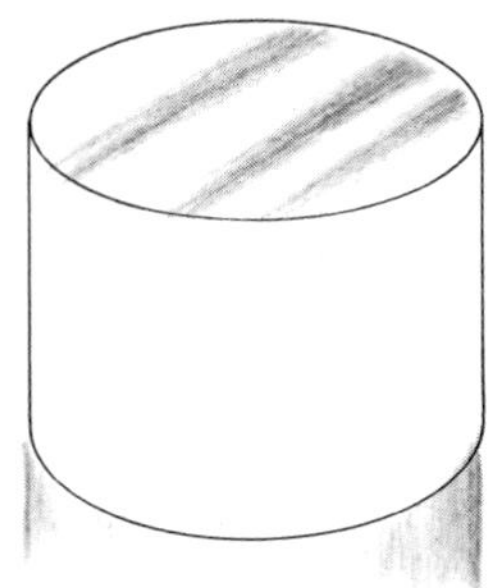

Exercise 8f

Add reflections to the drawings that you made for Exercises 7a to 7d and 7f. Imagine each object is standing on a polished surface.

Examples

These examples have been shaded according to the methods outlined in the last chapter combined with the application of shadows and reflections as described in this chapter.

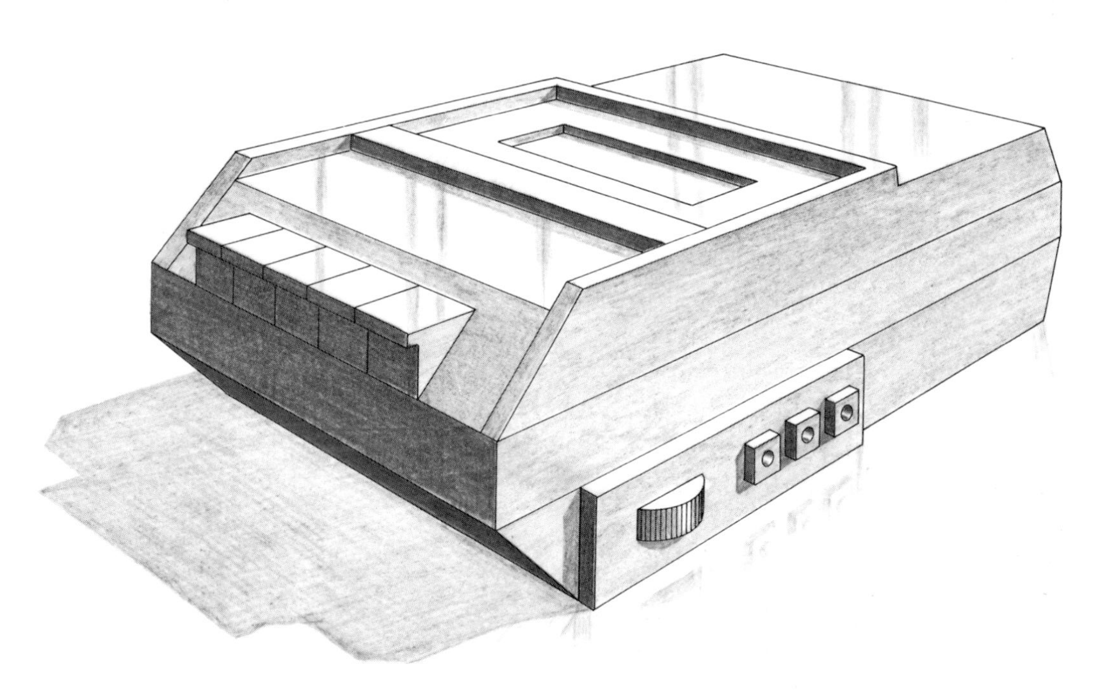

9 Texture

Because we can only see the outline shapes of these objects in silhouette it is impossible to tell what they are.

When light falls on them we can see that they are a tangerine and a golf ball. We can identify them because we can see each is roughly spherical and because, from past experience, we recognize their textures.

Texture can be of great help in conveying the form of the object and the material from which it is made. These drawings of a stone flake used by Iron-age man show texture applied incorrectly and correctly. Texture applied evenly over a drawing destroys the form of the object and is visually monotonous.

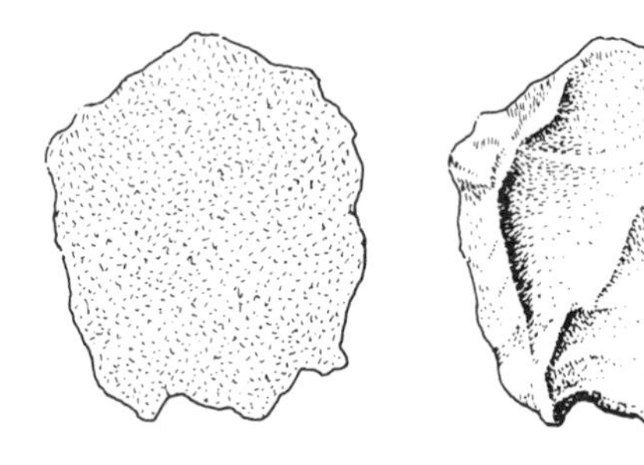

The drawings below show a selection of common articles that readily fit into the various categories of standard solids. Can you name these solids? (If not look back to Chapter 7.) The light comes from the top left and the texture has been applied taking this into account. When applying texture, always follow this rule: Apply least texture where most light is reflected and most texture where least light is reflected.

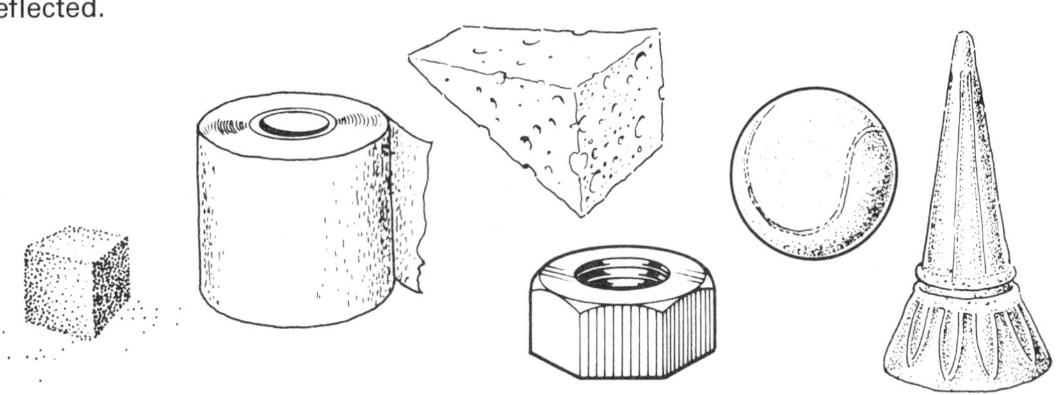

Textures represented by dots and round shapes

Dots or stippling on an illustration are an indication that the surface usually consists of a granular formation and hence lacks a smooth finish.

Sand

The sand that has been cast from the bucket takes the form of a cone that has been cut off across its top. The stippled texture follows the effect of light reflected from a conical shape.

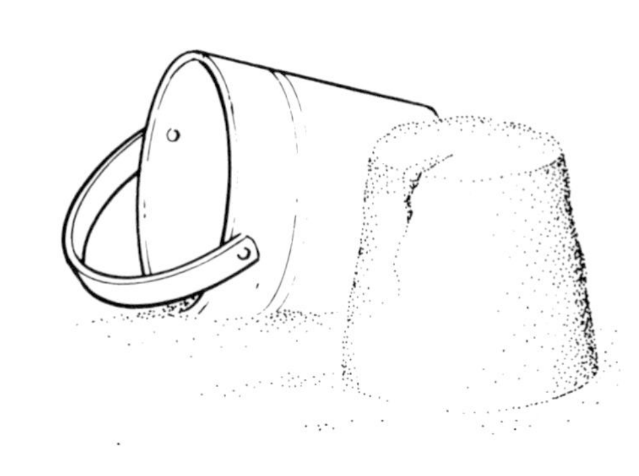

Sand-cast metals

The body of this bench vice would be cast in a sand mould and the impression of the particles of sand is retained. The technique for showing this effect on cast iron and other sand-cast metals is light stippling.

Rubber

Although rubber may be quite smooth it is not highly reflective and the surface appears rather dull. Medium to heavy stippling can be used to convey this impression while the form is retained by varying the density of the dots.

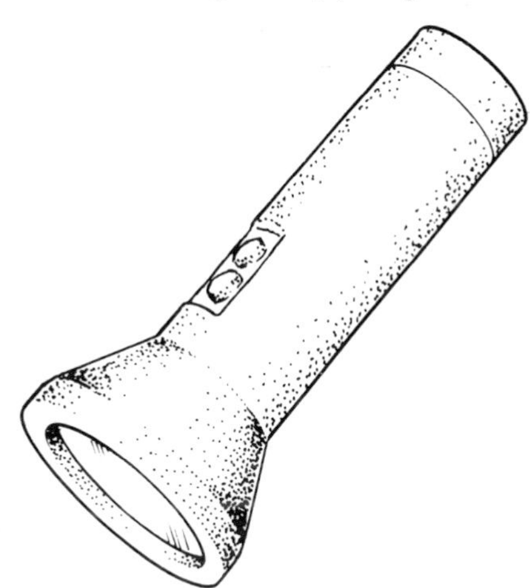

Concrete

Concrete contains larger stones in the form of ballast as well as the basic sand and cement mix. Some of these stones will show on the surface of the concrete object as well as any air bubbles that may appear on the surface as the concrete is setting. The drawing of the litter bin shows this as well as the normal sand stipple.

Polystyrene

This is a cellular material, rather than one which is formed by granules, and can be represented by small round and elliptical shapes as shown on the drawing of the dummy.

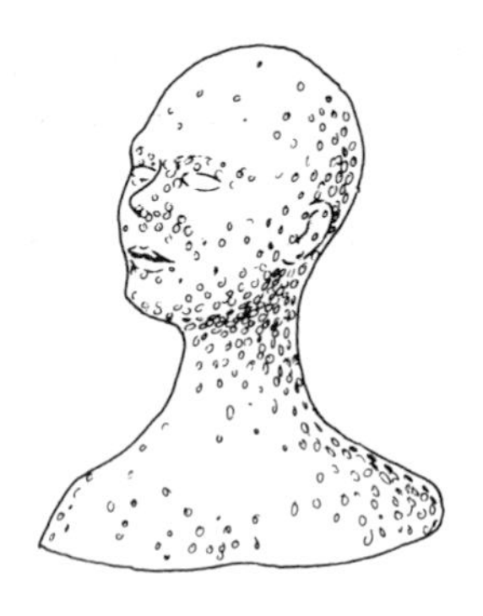

Exercise 9a

1 Draw the orange and the golf ball shown on page 70. Use only dots and lines to convey an impression of the surface texture and form. Remember to apply texture in the areas of least reflected light.

2 Find a stone that has been broken or chipped (a flintstone would be ideal for this exercise).
Using the drawing on page 70 as a guide, apply thin short lines to show the change in direction of the surfaces of the stone. You will be able to see these more clearly if you shine a light across the stone at a low angle.

3 This drawing represents a piece of rubber hosepipe. Copy it about twice this size and use heavy stippling to convey the texture and form.

Textures represented by lines

Glass and plastics

These materials are shown to be smooth by indicating some surface reflections. The reflections can be simplified to a number of thin tapering lines. The lines are set at an angle so as not to be confused with the edges of the object. This is a different effect to the reflections produced by shading on page 68.

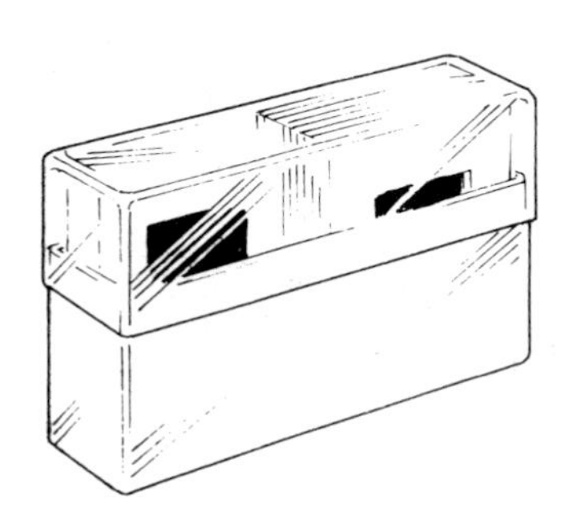

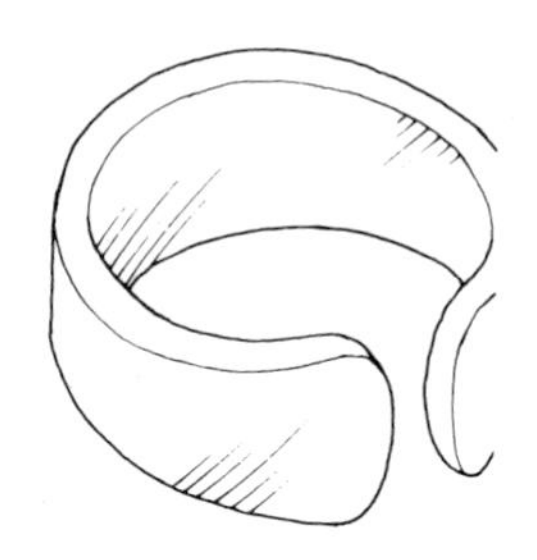

When this treatment is applied to clear plastic and glass, some indication of what can be seen through the clear material is required. The objects behind the transparent surface can be drawn with a thin line that is broken to reinforce the loss of detail.

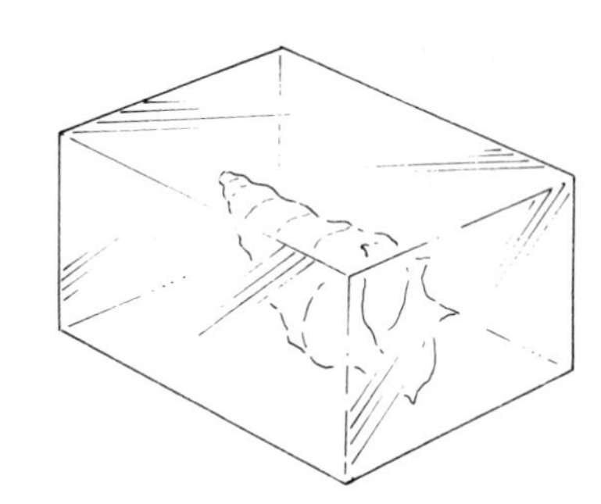

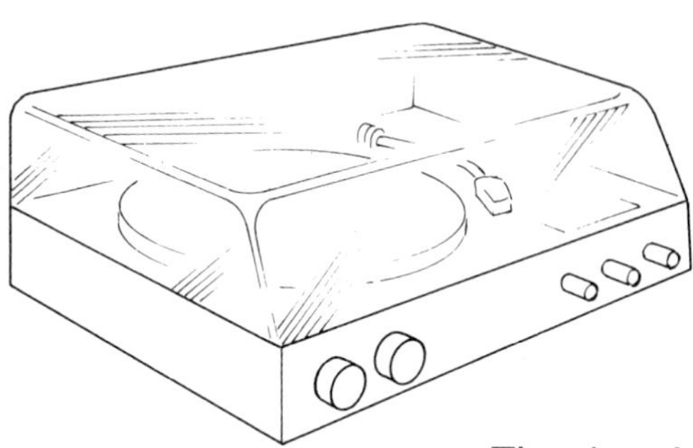

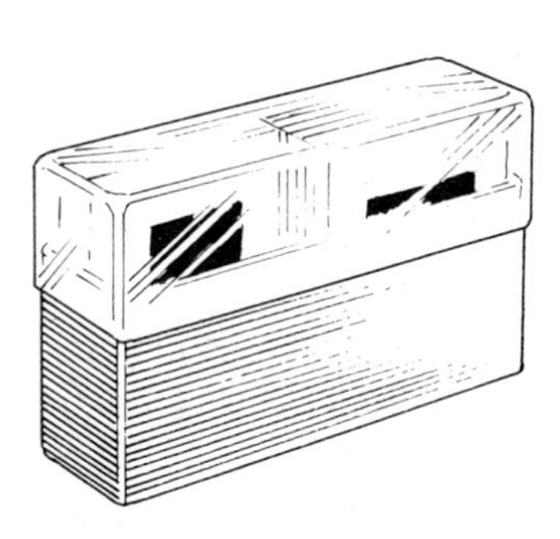

The drawing of the slide box indicates how to deal with reflections falling over a dark surface. White lines are left where the reflection lines would be lost against the dark areas.
The method used for rendering the plastic case is the same as shown below for machined metal.

Metal

A series of evenly spaced lines are drawn which follow the form of the object. This type of rendering is called 'form shading' and the number of lines that are drawn depends on the amount of light that is reflected from the surface, giving a similar impression of form to that shown in Chapter 7.

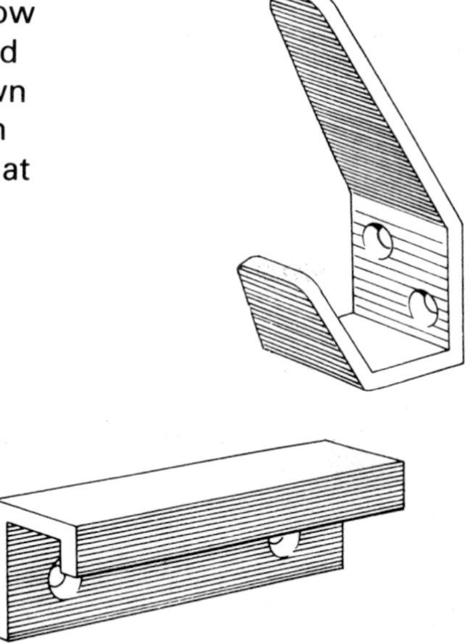

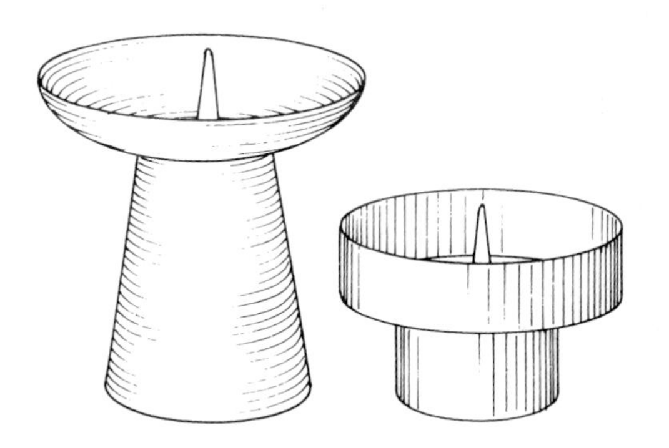

Wood

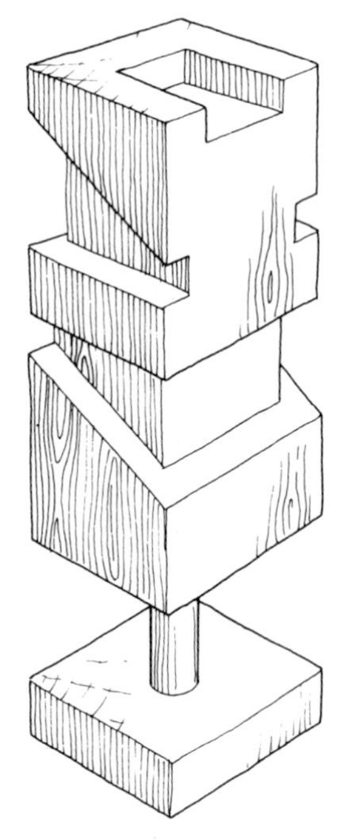

Lines that correspond to the grain structure are used. Although the grain differs in detail among the various species of timber, for the purposes of illustration there are three types of grain pattern, as shown:

1. End grain showing growth rings and medullary rays.
2. Side grain that tends to be rather fine.
3. Facing grain which is broad and wavy and is used for decorative effects on furniture.

The spacing of the grain may be altered to take account of reflected light and thus ensures that the impression of a three-dimensional solid is conveyed.

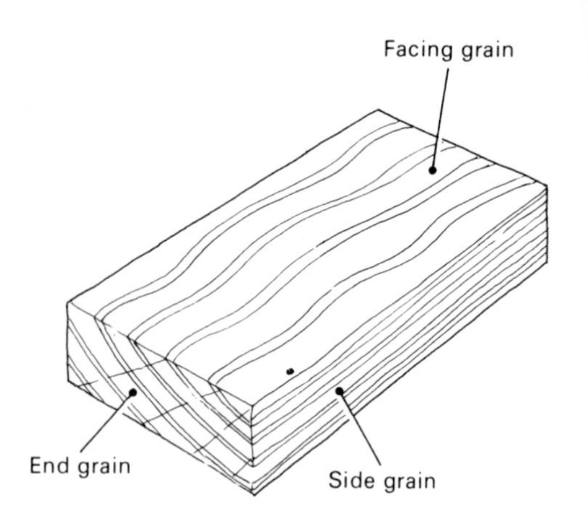

Exercise 9b

Make drawings of these objects about twice this printed size. Using lines only, show the surface texture and form of each.

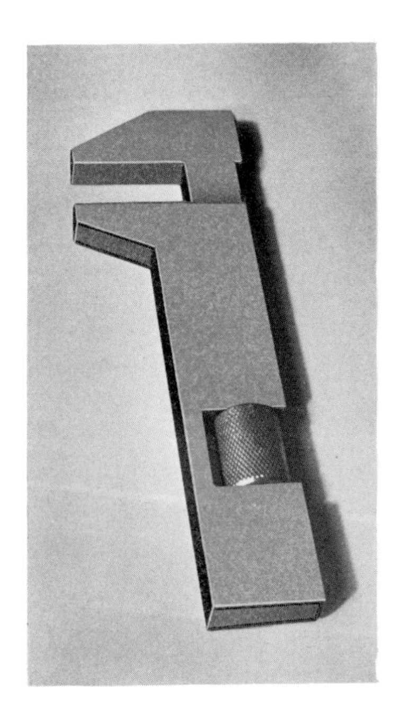

Textures represented by solid areas

Some surfaces are so smooth that no texture is evident. The reflections that can be seen in these surfaces are indicated by solid areas of shading.

Chrome plated and polished metals

A polished metal cylinder can be represented by heavy black lines that reduce in width as the surface turns towards the light. This is called 'bar shading' and follows the outline of the form, as you can see from the examples.

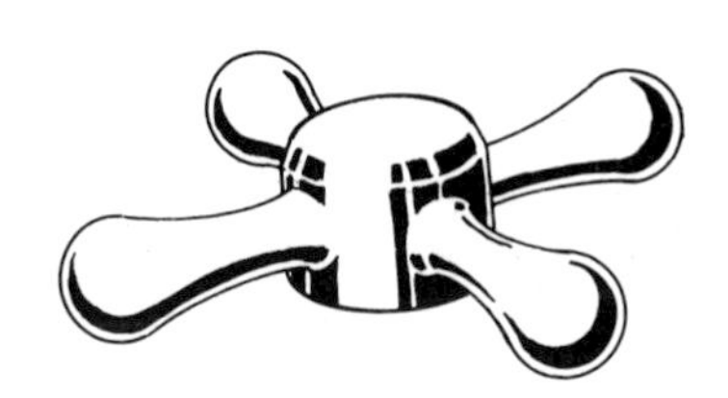

A thin strip can be left inside the outline of curved surfaces to help to emphasize the roundness. This strip is caused by light that is reflected back from other surrounding surfaces.

Opaque plastic

This material can be shown as a solid colour except for white bands which indicate reflections in the surface. These reflections are placed at an angle so that they do not become confused with the outlines of the object.

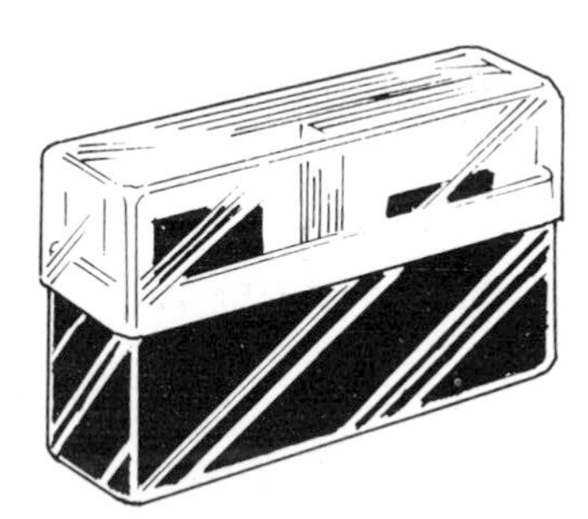

This type of rendering is particularly effective when the surface is coloured.

Exercise 9c

Draw this napkin ring about twice this size. Use solid areas of shading to convey the form of the ring and to indicate its highly reflective surfaces.

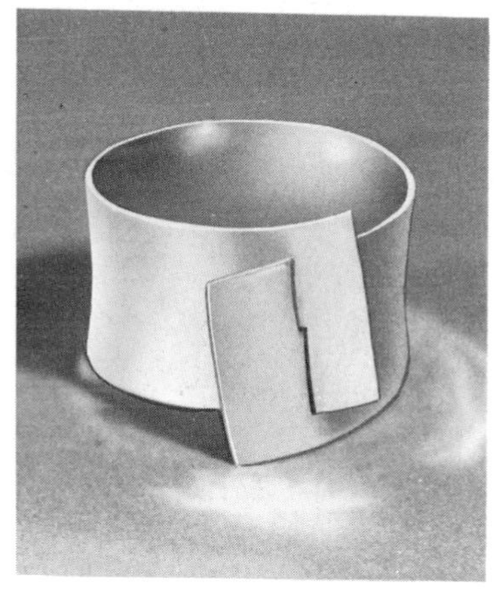

Examples

The cases of the camera and the tape recorder have been made with a special texture on some of the surfaces to ensure that the articles can be held without fear of slipping. This texture has been drawn with irregular closed shapes and some dots:

The other surfaces have been rendered according to the methods shown in this chapter. Part of the top of the tape recorder has been moulded to incorporate a granular texture.

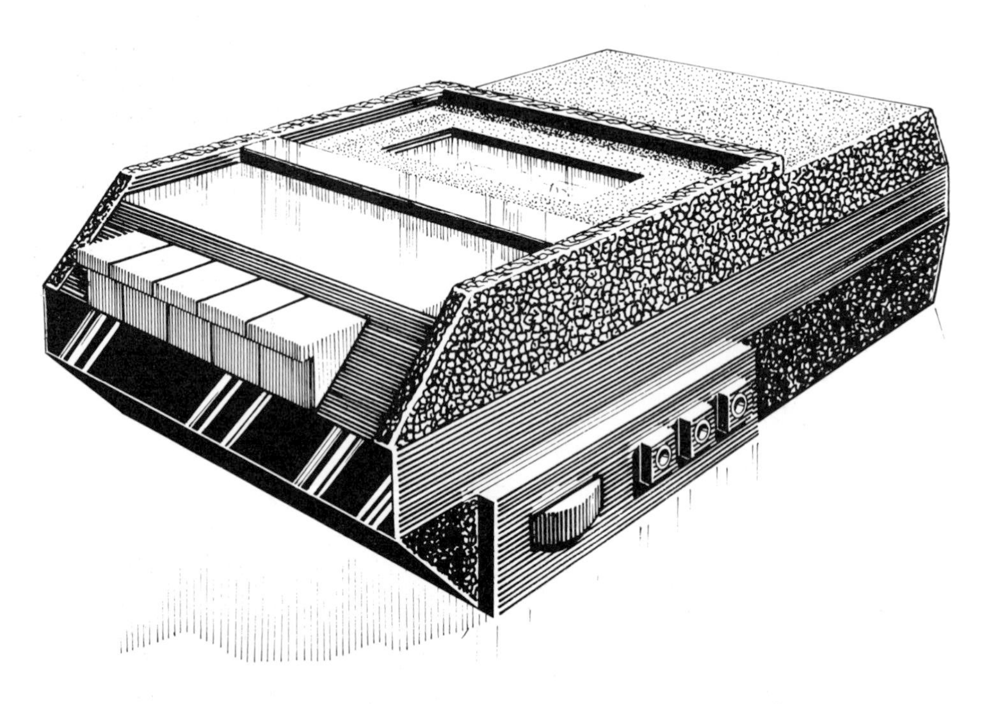

10 The exploded view

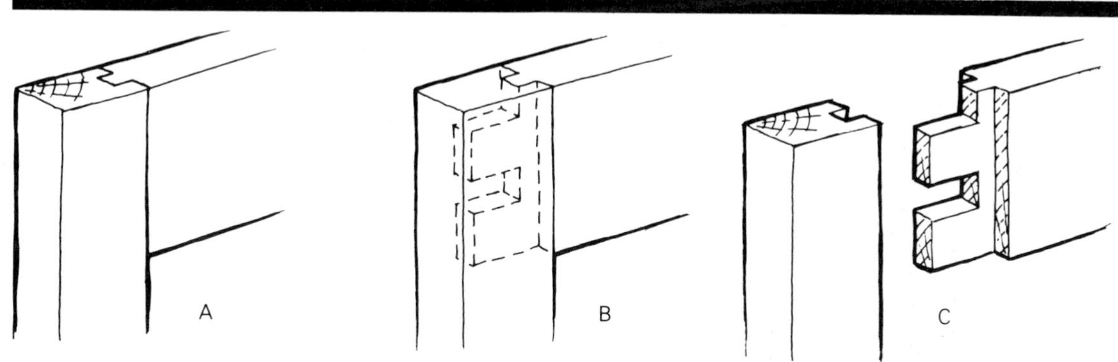

These three views show alternative ways of drawing the same joint. Drawing A, the assembled exterior view, gives no indication of the shape inside. Drawing B is also an external view of the joint, but in this case the hidden internal details are shown with dashed lines. In view C, the joint appears as if its parts have been taken or **blown** apart along a natural line of movement. This latter drawing is known as an **exploded view**. It is the clearest of the three drawings since the details of the joint are exposed and are more realistic.

In an exploded view the components should be shown in such a way that their relationship to each other is obvious, so that anyone wishing to reassemble them can do so in the correct order without confusion. When the parts of this typical bicycle lamp are 'exploded', they follow two lines of natural movement. The bulb, reflector and glass assembly follow one axis in their correct sequence, whilst the battery and switch assembly are drawn along another.

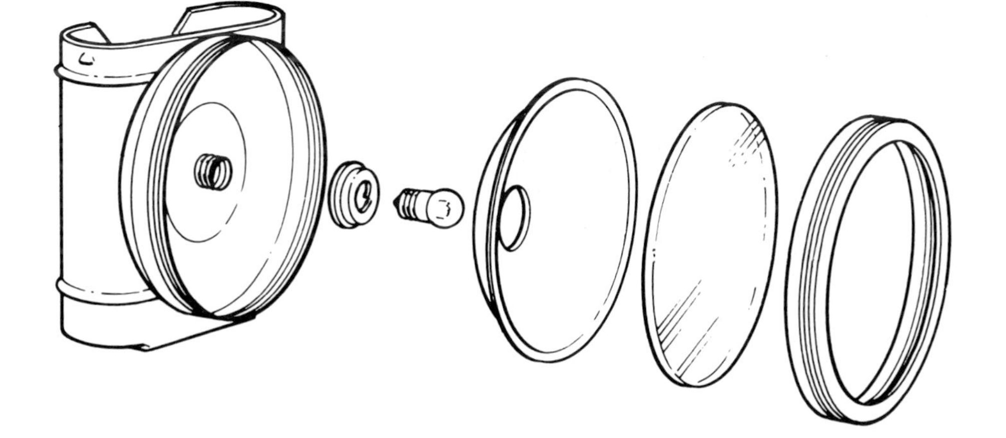

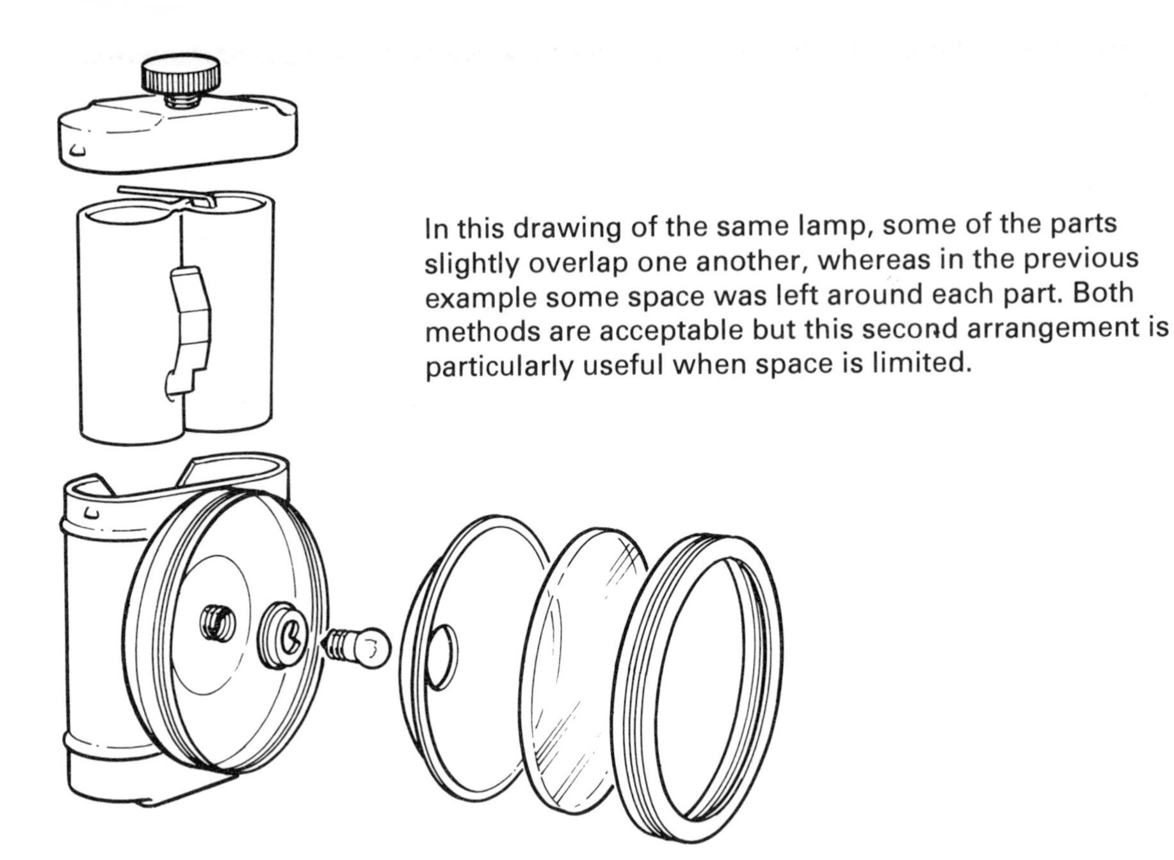

In this drawing of the same lamp, some of the parts slightly overlap one another, whereas in the previous example some space was left around each part. Both methods are acceptable but this second arrangement is particularly useful when space is limited.

Exercise 10a

1 Find examples of exploded views and identify the natural lines of movement using felt-tipped pens or coloured pencils, etc.
The instruction leaflets in model or construction kits and the illustrations in car or home maintenance magazines are ideal for this exercise.

2 Obtain one of the following objects and make a drawing showing the parts 'exploded' along the natural lines of movement.
(a) A torch.
(b) A pencil box clearly showing the construction of the joints.
(c) An electric plug.
(d) A woodworker's hand drill.
(e) A model car.
(If you cannot get any of these objects, find one of your own that contains at least six parts.)

Answers

Note that many of the answers shown are not the only correct solutions to the exercises since, in many cases, these depend on the viewpoint you have chosen or, as in the later exercises, the position in which you have placed the light source.

Exercise 1a

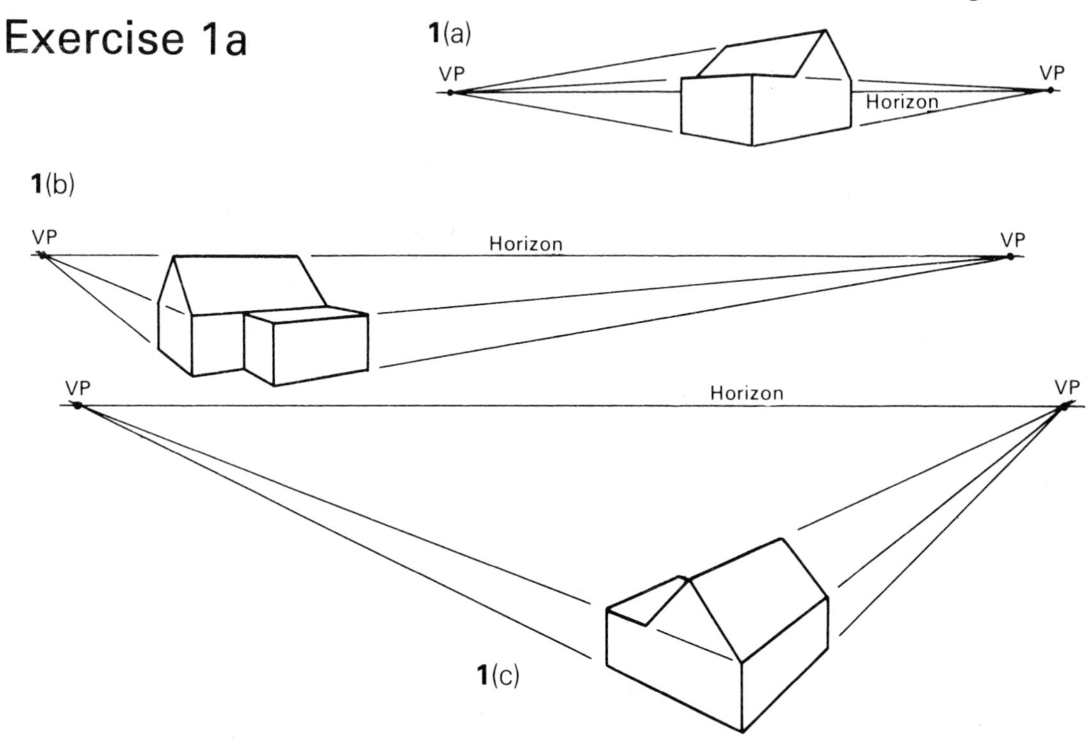

Exercise 1c

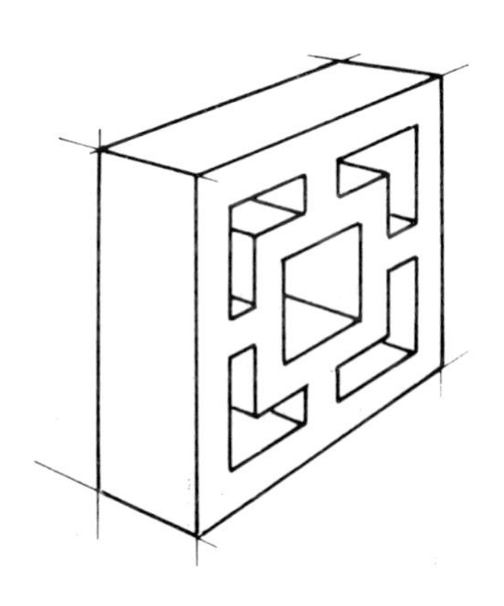

Exercise 1d

1 (a) Two-point perspective. (b) Three-point perspective. (c) One-point perspective. (d) Two-point perspective.

2 (a) 4 vanishing points.

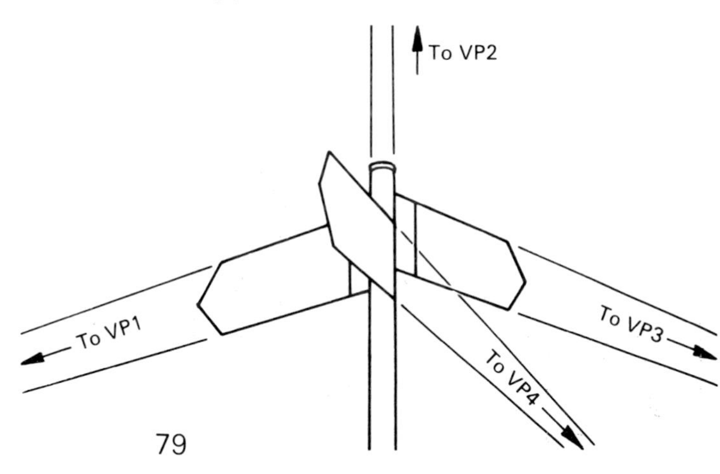

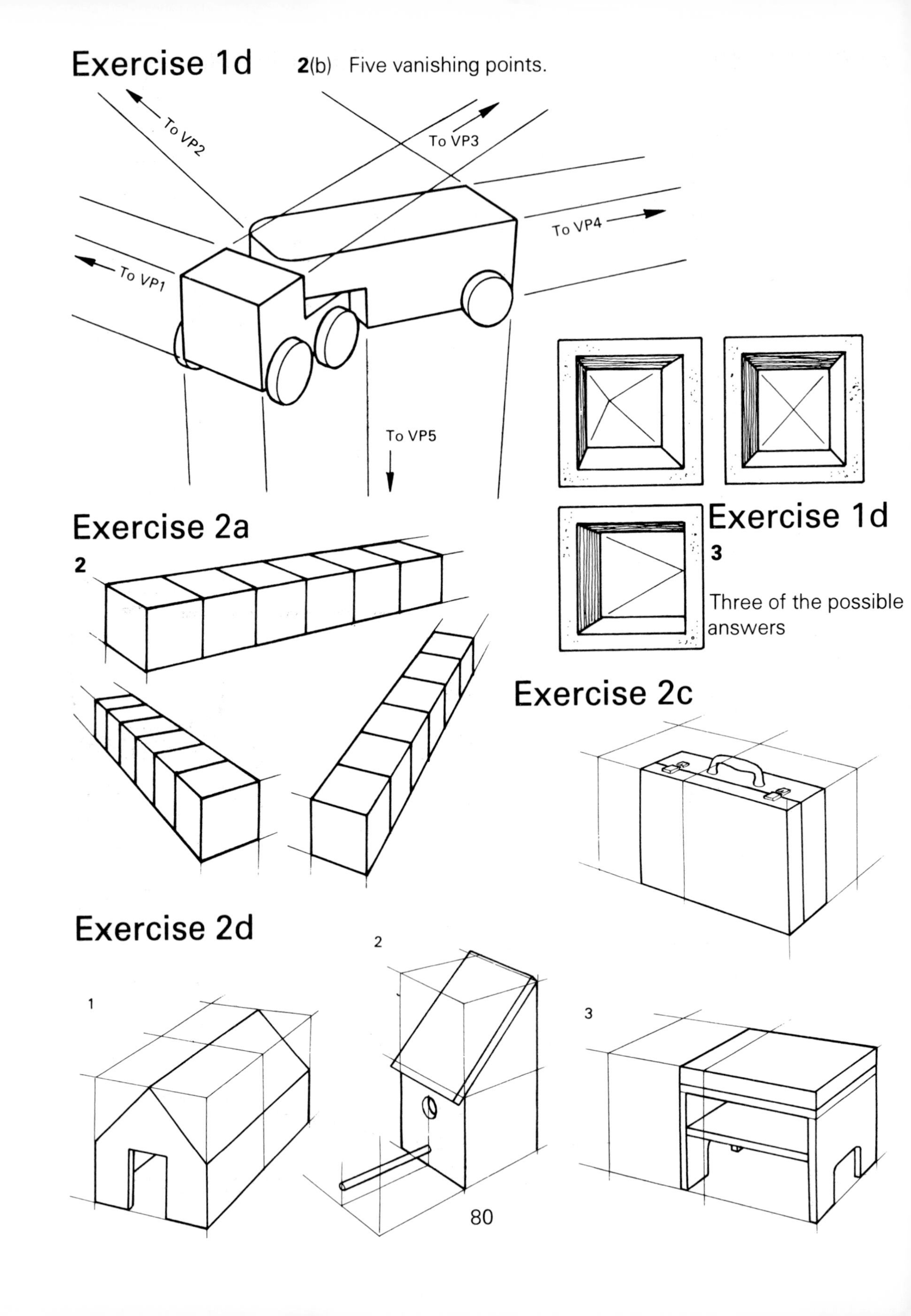
Exercise 1d
2(b) Five vanishing points.
To VP2
To VP3
To VP4
To VP1
To VP5
Exercise 2a
2
Exercise 1d
3
Three of the possible answers
Exercise 2c
Exercise 2d
2
1
3

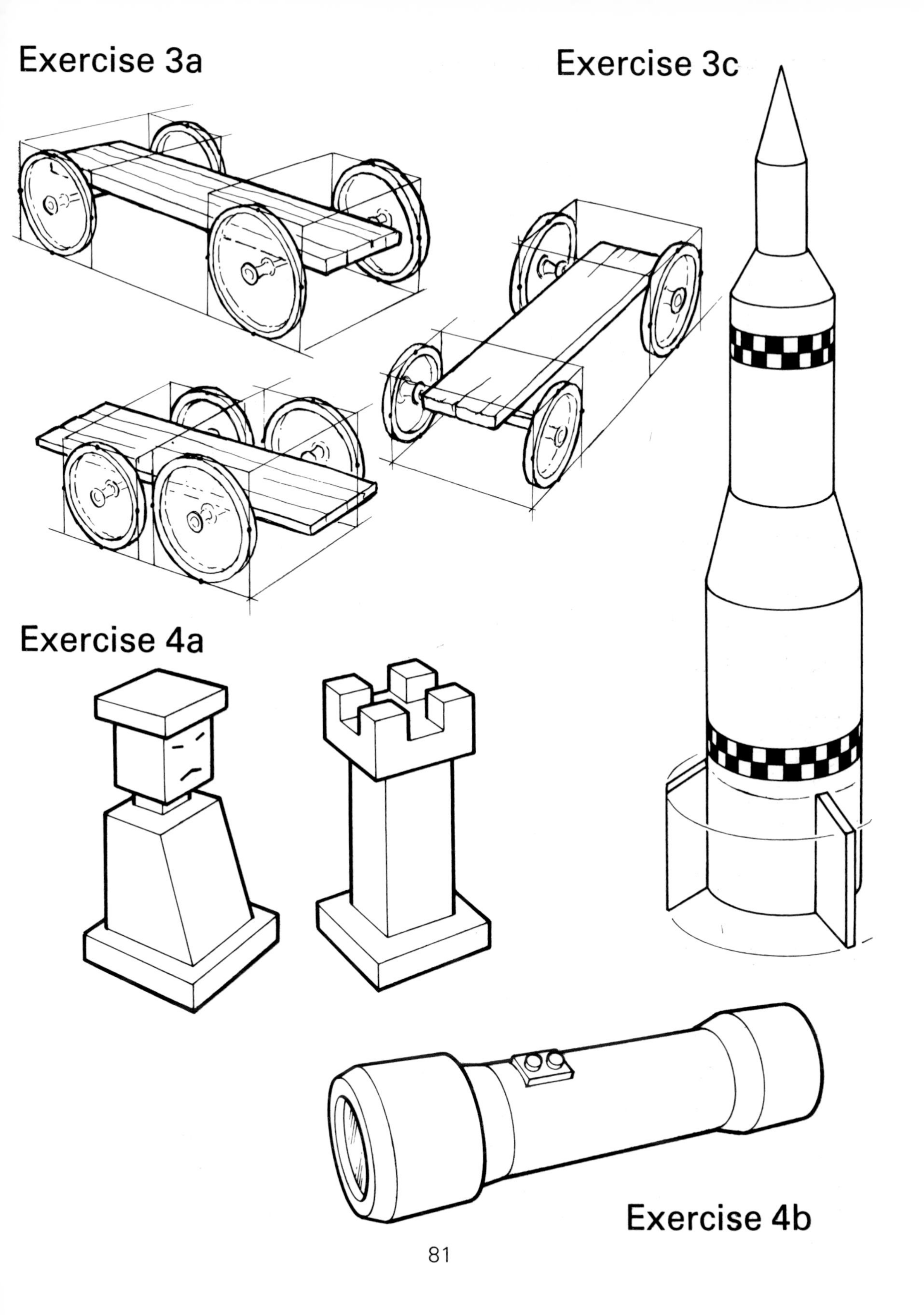
Exercise 3a
Exercise 3c
Exercise 4a
Exercise 4b

Exercise 5a

1

3

5

2

4

6

Exercise 5b

1

2

Exercise 5c

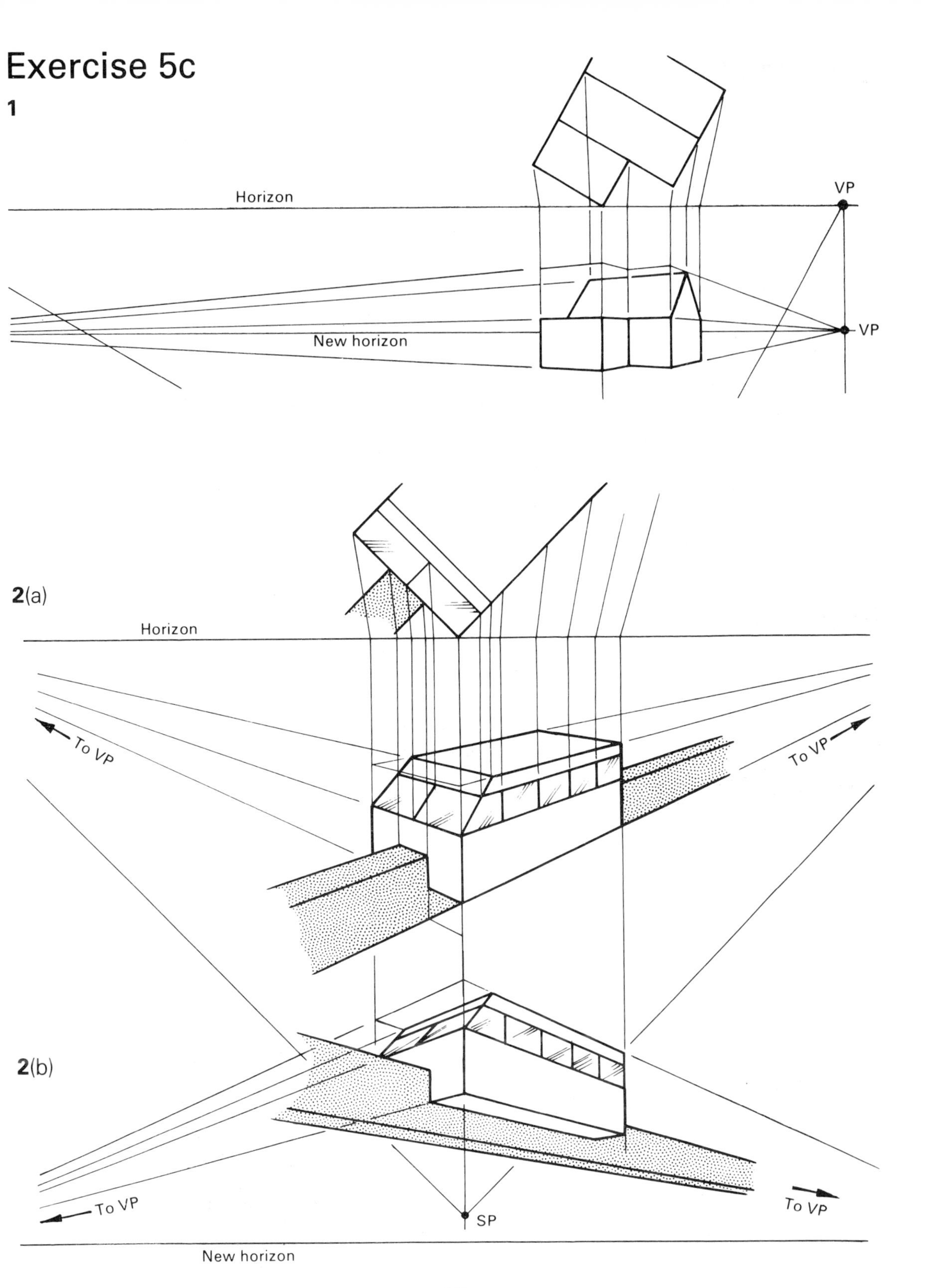
1
Horizon
VP
New horizon
VP
2(a)
Horizon
To VP
To VP
2(b)
To VP
To VP
SP
New horizon

Exercise 6a

1

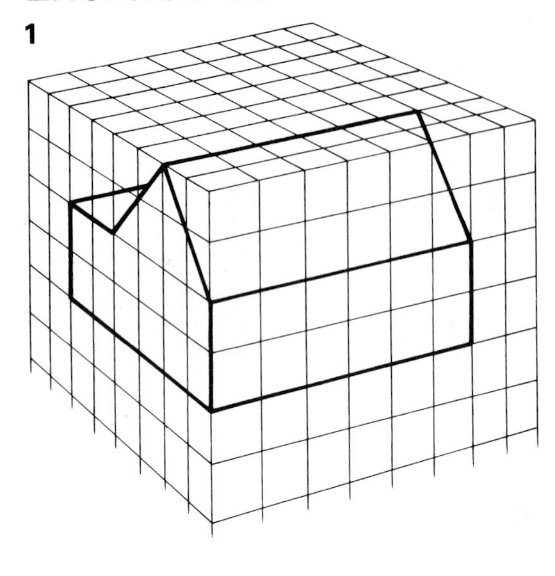

2

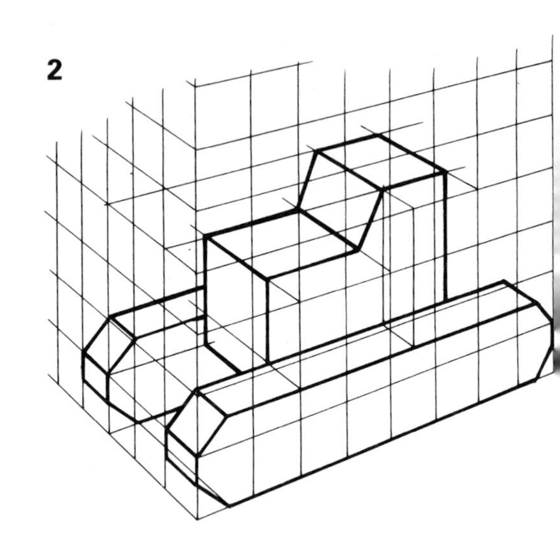

Exercise 6b

0

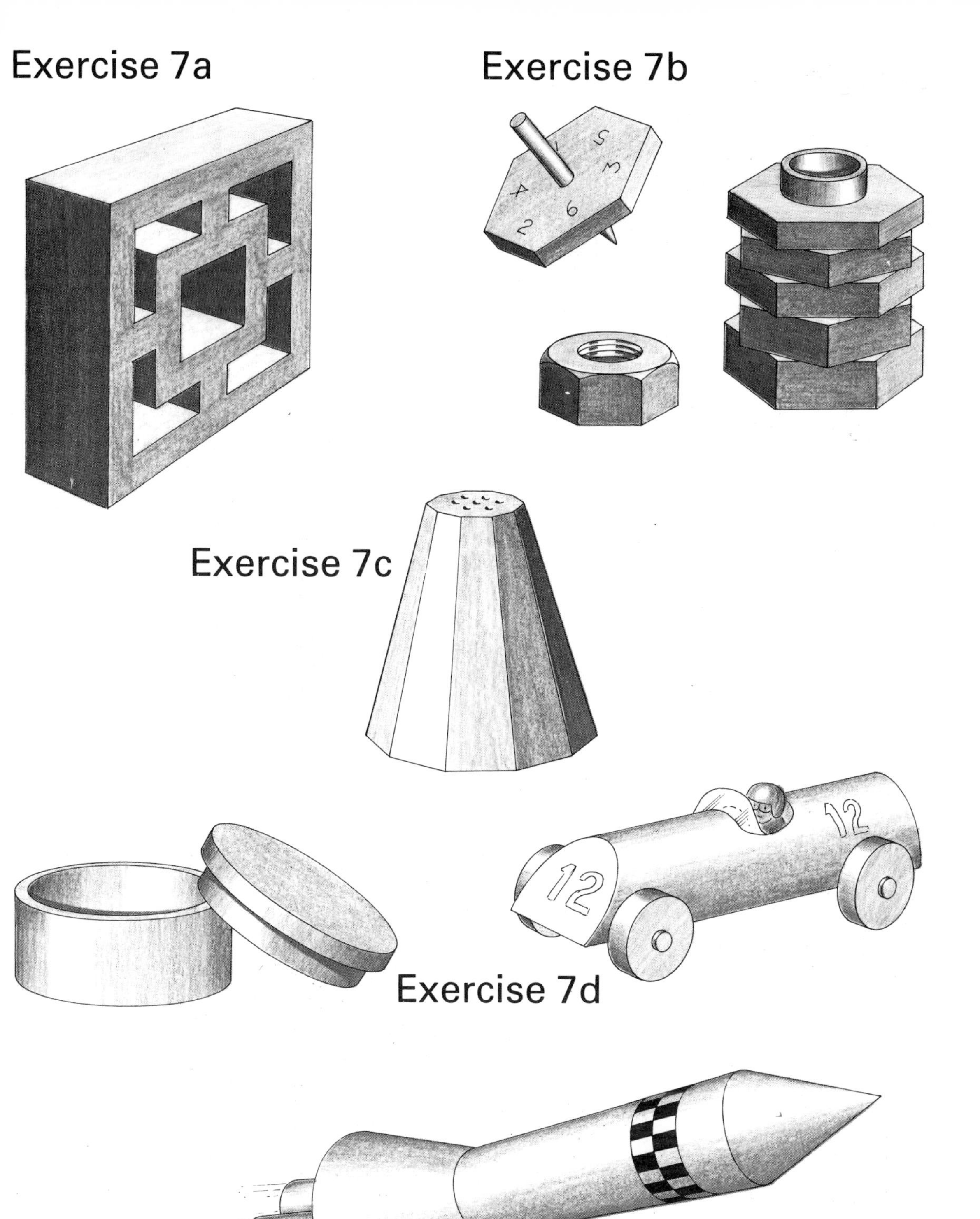
Exercise 7a
Exercise 7b
1
5
3
4
6
2
Exercise 7c
12
12
Exercise 7d

Exercise 7e

Exercise 7f

Exercise 7g

Exercise 8a

1. A horizontal surface—the ground or floor.
2. A horizontal and a vertical surface—a floor and a wall.
3. A convex surface—a large pipe or a barrel.
4. A series of alternating horizontal and vertical surfaces—steps or stairs.
5. A concave surface—inside a cylindrical tunnel.
6. A horizontal surface which suddenly falls away—the edge of a wharf or a dock.
7. The following series of surfaces: horizontal, short vertical, short horizontal, short vertical, horizontal—a low wall.
8. A horizontal surface which suddenly drops—a short distance away a vertical wall followed by a horizontal surface at the same level as the first—a channel or a trench.

Exercise 8b

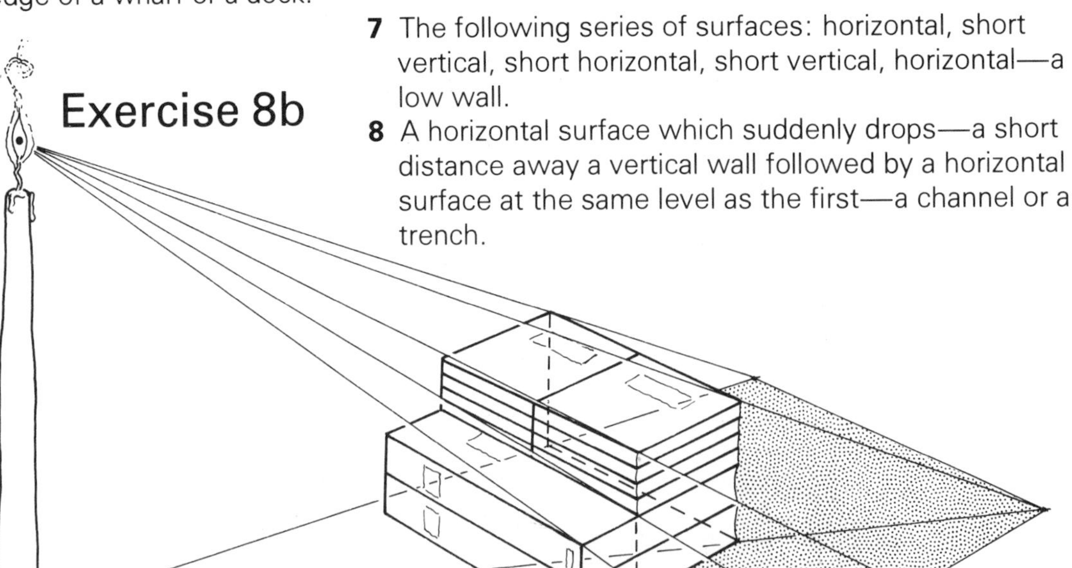

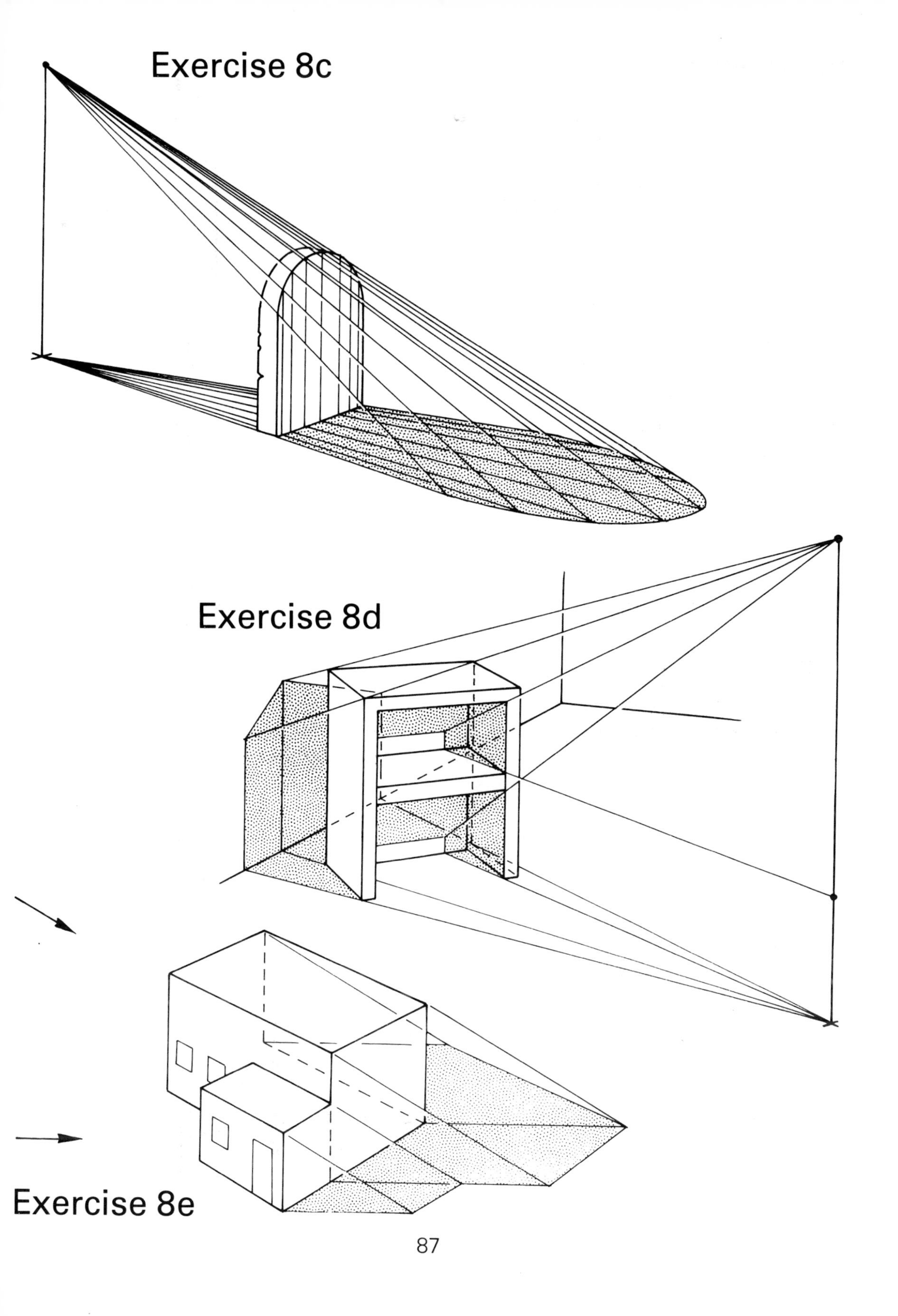
Exercise 8c
Exercise 8d
Exercise 8e

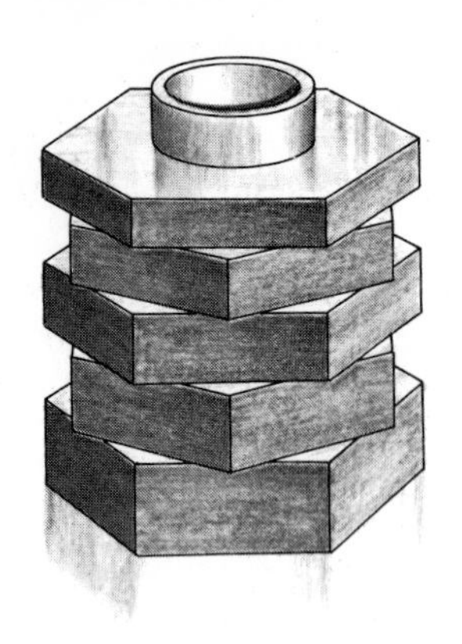

Exercise 8f

This is one of the answers for this exercise. Note the reflections in the top surface from the tube and other external objects. Reflections also occur in the surface on which the object stands.

Exercise 9a

1

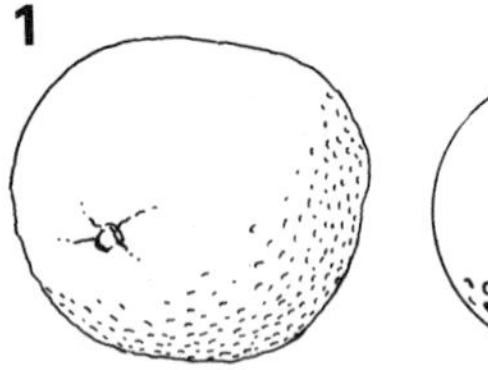

3

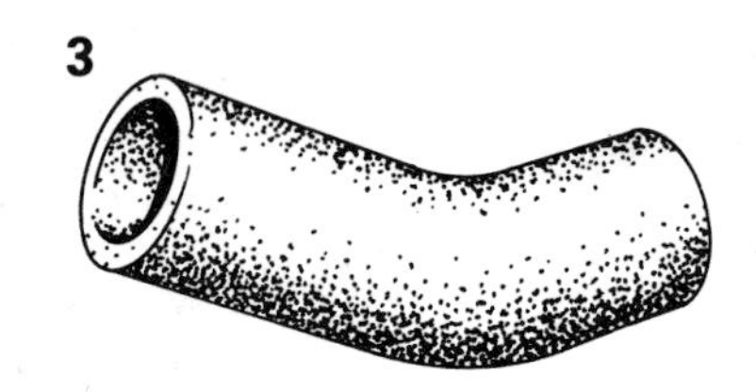

Exercise 9b

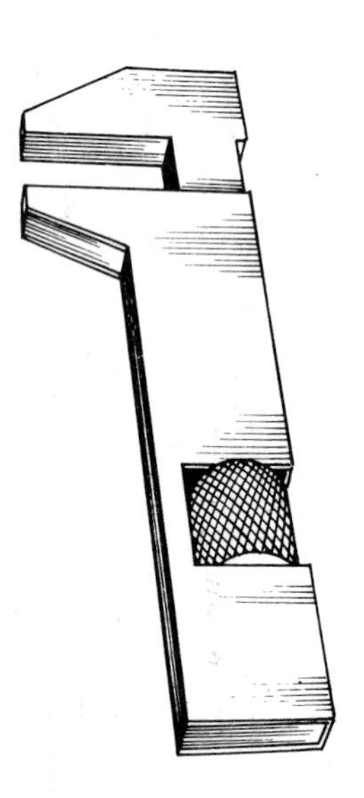

Exercise 9c